THE COMPLETE
JOHN DEERE

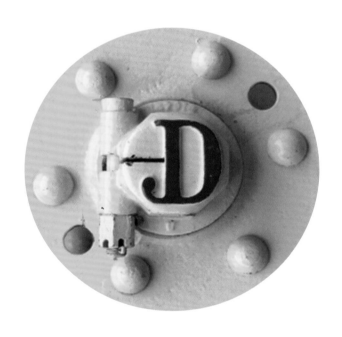

THE COMPLETE
JOHN DEERE

A MODEL-BY-MODEL HISTORY

PETER HENSHAW

Lowe & B. Hould
Publishers

This edition published in 2004 by Lowe & B. Hould publishers, an imprint of Borders, Inc.,
515 East Liberty, Ann Arbor, MI 48104. Lowe & B. Hould Publishers is a trademark of Borders Properties, Inc.

First published by MBI Publishing Company, Galtier Plaza, Suite 200, 380 Jackson Street, St. Paul, MN 55101-3885 USA

© Salamander Books Ltd., 2003, 2004

An imprint of Chrysalis Books Group

ISBN 0-681-16578-2

Credits

Editor: Katherine Edelston
Design, Layout and Reproduction: Q2A Solutions Ltd
Production: Ian Hughes

Printed in Thailand

Contents

Introduction

Tractors are not glamorous. Not in the way that motorcycles are glamorous. Or steam locomotives or biplanes. Farm tractors were designed and built to do a job of work. No more, no less. And yet, all over the world, old tractors are often held in great affection, especially by the people who spent their working lives sitting on one. Nowhere is this more true than in North America, where for countless small farmers their little Fordson, or Farmall, or John Deere was almost part of the family.

John Deere himself would probably have found that hard to understand. He was a practical man, the son of an English emigrant tailor who died when young John was just eight. So he had to make his own way in the world, but soon found it as he was apprenticed to a blacksmith from an early age. Here, John's talents flourished, and he soon earned a reputation for making shovels so well polished that they scoured themselves of soil.

In 1836, with a growing family to support, John Deere moved west to Grand Detour, which was then just a village about 100 miles west of Chicago. Here he would make his fortune, and his name.

Many farmers had settled this land, but were thinking of giving up and moving back east again. Why? The soil was so heavy and sticky that ploughs soon became hopelessly clogged. John Deere saw the problem, and made a finely finished steel plough out of a broken saw blade—it was so well polished that even the heavy soil just fell away. It was what every farmer needed, and for the rest of his life, John Deere never lacked for work.

His business grew. In 1841, 75 ploughs left the new works—ten years later, his expanded factory was producing 75 ploughs, every week. In 1879, over 40,000 walking ploughs alone were built, not to mention cultivators, harrows, and gang ploughs. John Deere never went to business school, but he knew that the way to survive was via expansion and constant improvement. When he died in 1886, his son Charles took over a massive concern that offered every type of farm equipment.

A decade or so later, many companies were rushing into the new market for internal combustion engine tractors. Not John Deere & Co. Some of these tractors

Above: A well used, but well loved, John Deere 50. Generations of farmers viewed their old "Johnny Poppers" with great affection.

worked, many did not, leaving behind ruined businesses, disillusioned shareholders, and disgruntled customers. Not until 1912, did the Deere Board finally decide to, "produce a tractor plough." Even then, there was no rush. Six years of experiments, false starts, and false dawns followed until the company did what perhaps it should have done in the first place. It found a tractor that was already tried, tested, and well proven, and bought the company that made it. From 1918, as new owner of the Waterloo Gasoline Traction Engine Company, John

how did this happen? On the face of it, John Deere was a conservative, family-run organization. For its first 145 years of its existence (up to 1982) the company was headed by a member of the Deere family, either by blood or by marriage, and family dynasties don't always make for dynamic leadership. As if to confirm it, John Deere stuck with the same simple twin-cylinder engine layout for years after its competitors moved on to fours and sixes. Of course, these simple, slow-revving "Johnny Poppers" inspired an intensely loyal band of owners, but by the time America entered World War II, they were looking very old-fashioned.

There's an interesting parallel with Harley-Davidson, another American industrial icon. That too was family run for years, and stuck with a tried and trusted design long after the competition had moved on. But there was a crucial difference: Harley-Davidson made motorcycles, leisure toys which are often bought with a dream in mind— being outdated, but part of American folklore, became a positive marketing tool, and one that Harley-Davidson made good use of. Today, it thrives.

That route was never open to John Deere. Tractors, for all the affection in which they might be held, are ultimately bought for hard-headed reasons. So to survive, Deere had to leave Johnny Popper behind, and they did in no uncertain terms, replacing the entire range overnight with the ultra-modern New Generation of 1960. That wholesale change took corporate courage, but they made the leap that had to be made, and survived. And that's why tractors are still being built in Waterloo, Ohio today, 85 years after John Deere first went into the tractor making business.

Deere was finally in the tractor business. So it was no pioneer, but that did Deere no harm. Eventually it rose to become the industry leader, after years of playing second fiddle to arch-rival International. When everyone hit hard times in the 1980s, John Deere was the only major US tractor maker to come through it without merger, takeover or complete closure. In 1988 it sold over $1 billion worth of industrial and agricultural machinery. But

Peter Henshaw
Sherborne, Dorset,
United Kingdom, 2003

Waterloo Boy Model R

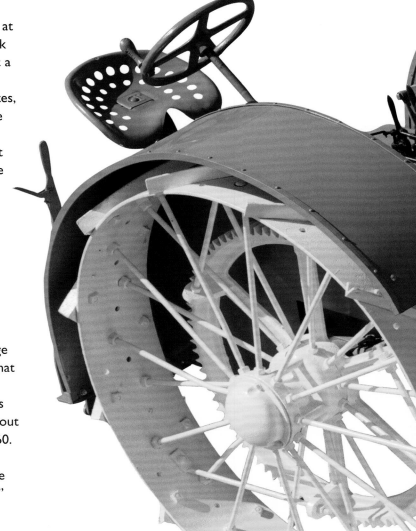

Waterloo Boy Model R (1914)

Engine type Twin-cylinder ohv, water-cooled

Fuel type Kerosene

Bore x stroke 5.5 x 7.0in

Capacity 333ci (5.2 liters)

Rated speed 750rpm

TRANSMISSION

Transmission type Gear drive

Speeds 1F/1R

Speed range 2.5mph

DIMENSIONS

Factory weight n/a

Tested weight n/a

Length 143in

Width 72in

Height 63in

Wheel size F 28 x 6

Wheel size R 52 x 10

Fuel tank (US gallons, main/aux) 20/1

Cooling capacity (US gallons) 8.5

PERFORMANCE

Power (at PTO) 25hp

Power (at drawbar) 12hp

Fuel efficiency n/a

This was the tractor which started it all, though if truth be told, it wasn't really a John Deere tractor at all, but a Waterloo. The Waterloo's roots stretched back to 1892, when John Froelich, a threshing operator, built a gasoline tractor to replace the steamer he was using.

It worked well and, together with business associates, Froelich formed the Waterloo Gasoline Traction Engine Company to enable him to put it into production. Unfortunately, the production tractors (there were just four) failed to match the success of that first prototype and Froelich left the company, which then switched to producing stationary engines only.

But Waterloo didn't let the tractor idea go to waste and by 1914, with the American tractor market blossoming, it was put back into production. The company had also produced a few tractors before then, such as the half-track "Sure Grip," all-wheel-drive Model C and four-cylinder TP, but it struck gold with the much smaller and simpler Model R. With just two cylinders and two-wheel-drive, the R held the advantage that it was relatively lightweight and cheap—exactly what farmers of the time wanted.

Even more significant for the John Deere story was that it provided the foundation of the twin-cylinder layout that the company would stay faithful to right up to 1960. Its big cylinders (5.5 x 7 inches on the early tractors) were slow turning but torquey, which proved to be one of the greatest strengths of the Deere'"Johnny Popper"

Below: Note the chain steering set up on this early Model R—automotive-type rod steering was adopted later.

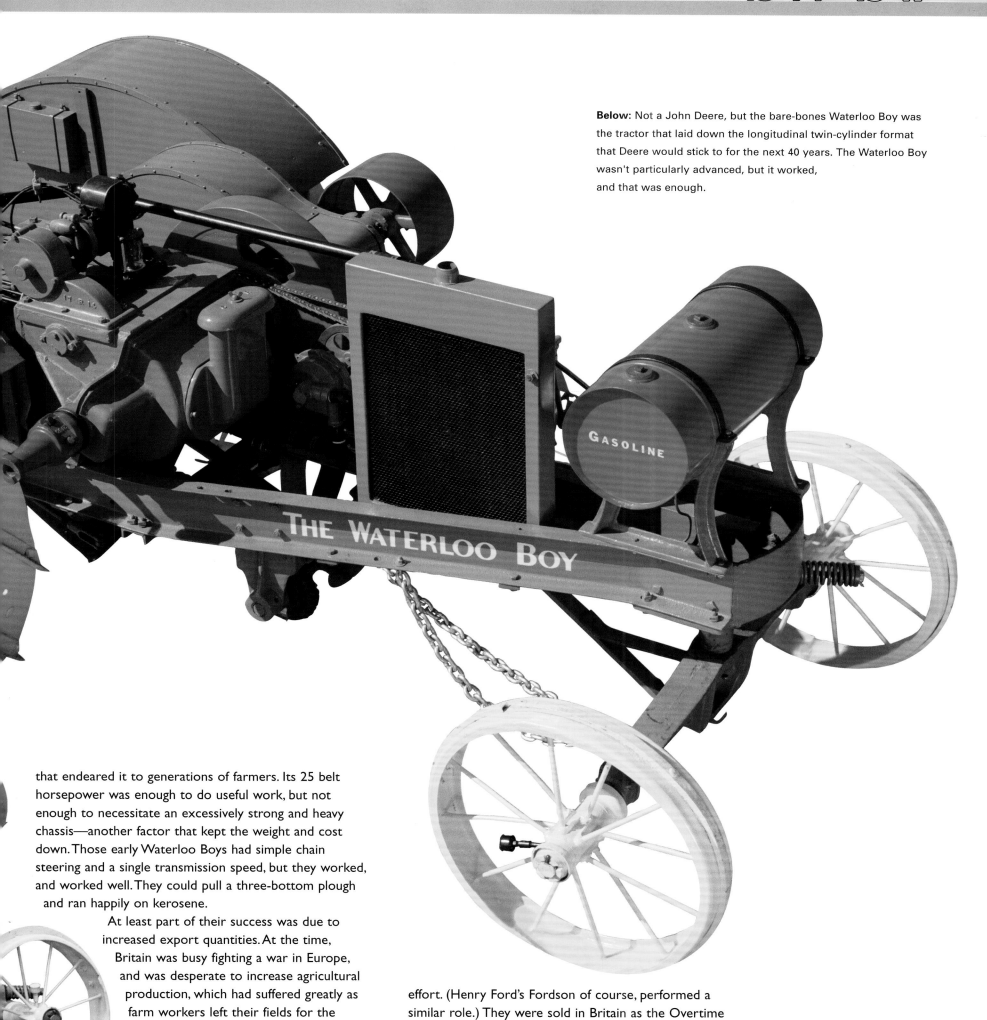

Below: Not a John Deere, but the bare-bones Waterloo Boy was the tractor that laid down the longitudinal twin-cylinder format that Deere would stick to for the next 40 years. The Waterloo Boy wasn't particularly advanced, but it worked, and that was enough.

THE WATERLOO BOY

GASOLINE

that endeared it to generations of farmers. Its 25 belt horsepower was enough to do useful work, but not enough to necessitate an excessively strong and heavy chassis—another factor that kept the weight and cost down. Those early Waterloo Boys had simple chain steering and a single transmission speed, but they worked, and worked well. They could pull a three-bottom plough and ran happily on kerosene.

At least part of their success was due to increased export quantities. At the time, Britain was busy fighting a war in Europe, and was desperate to increase agricultural production, which had suffered greatly as farm workers left their fields for the Western Front, and the country also feared the effects of a naval blocade.

Tractors were the obvious answer and consequently 4,000 Waterloo Boys would be shipped across the Atlantic to help Britain's war effort. (Henry Ford's Fordson of course, performed a similar role.) They were sold in Britain as the Overtime tractor—the Irish agent, incidentally, was none other than Harry Ferguson! Whatever its name, the Waterloo Boy was one of the best selling tractors of its time, and can claim to be the ancestor of every subsequent John Deere tractor up to 1959.

Waterloo Boy Model N

SPECIFICATIONS

Waterloo Boy Model N

Engine type Twin-cylinder ohv, water-cooled

Fuel type Kerosene

Bore x stroke 6.5 x 7.0in

Capacity 464ci (7.6 liters)

Rated speed 750rpm

Carburetor Schebler Model D

TRANSMISSION

Transmission type Sliding gear, chain final

Speeds 2F/1R

Speed range 2.25-3.0mph

DIMENSIONS

Factory weight 6,183lb

Tested weight n/a

Length 132in

Width 72in

Height 63in

Wheel size F 28 x 6

Wheel size R 52 x 12

Fuel tank (US gallons, main/aux) 20/1

Cooling capacity (US gallons) 8.5

PERFORMANCE

Power (at PTO) 25hp

Power (at drawbar) 16hp

Fuel efficiency 6.83hp/hr per gallon

Above: Chain steering, but a two-speed transmission, on this pen and ink sketch of a Waterloo Boy.

So the Waterloo Boy was a great success. This hadn't gone unnoticed by John Deere, which by this time was a giant of the agicultural machinery industry—all it lacked was a tractor. Throughout its history, the company had expanded by acquisition. It would "talent spot" successful products, take over the firm that made them and incorporate them into the John Deere line up. By this means Deere grew from a single-line plough maker to offering a whole range of machinery.

The biggest growth area in the early 20th century was tractors, so it was natural that Deere should make a similar move here. Its own tentative attempts to build tractors in-house had met with little success, so it soon fell back on the policy that had served it so well in the past—buy up someone elses. In 1918 it did just that, taking over the Waterloo Gasoline Engine Company. This not only brought the Waterloo factory under the Deere umbrella (where John Deere tractors have been made ever since) but the Waterloo Boy as well.

Tractors were developing fast, and the Boy was beginning to look outdated, especially after Henry Ford came along with his lightweight, simple, and dirt cheap Fordson. Waterloo had been experimenting with enclosed transmissions (the next big thing in tractor design) but the prototype had final drive problems. So while work on the new tractor continued under John Deere (it would

eventually become the Model D) attention was also paid to updating the Waterloo Boy. The first renewed Model N Boy was shipped to a dealer in January 1918, and the changes effectively extended the tractor's life by another few years. The biggest news was a two-speed transmission to replace the old single-speed. Final drive was now by roller chain, and the old chain steering was junked in favor of an automotive-type rod linkage. There was a new

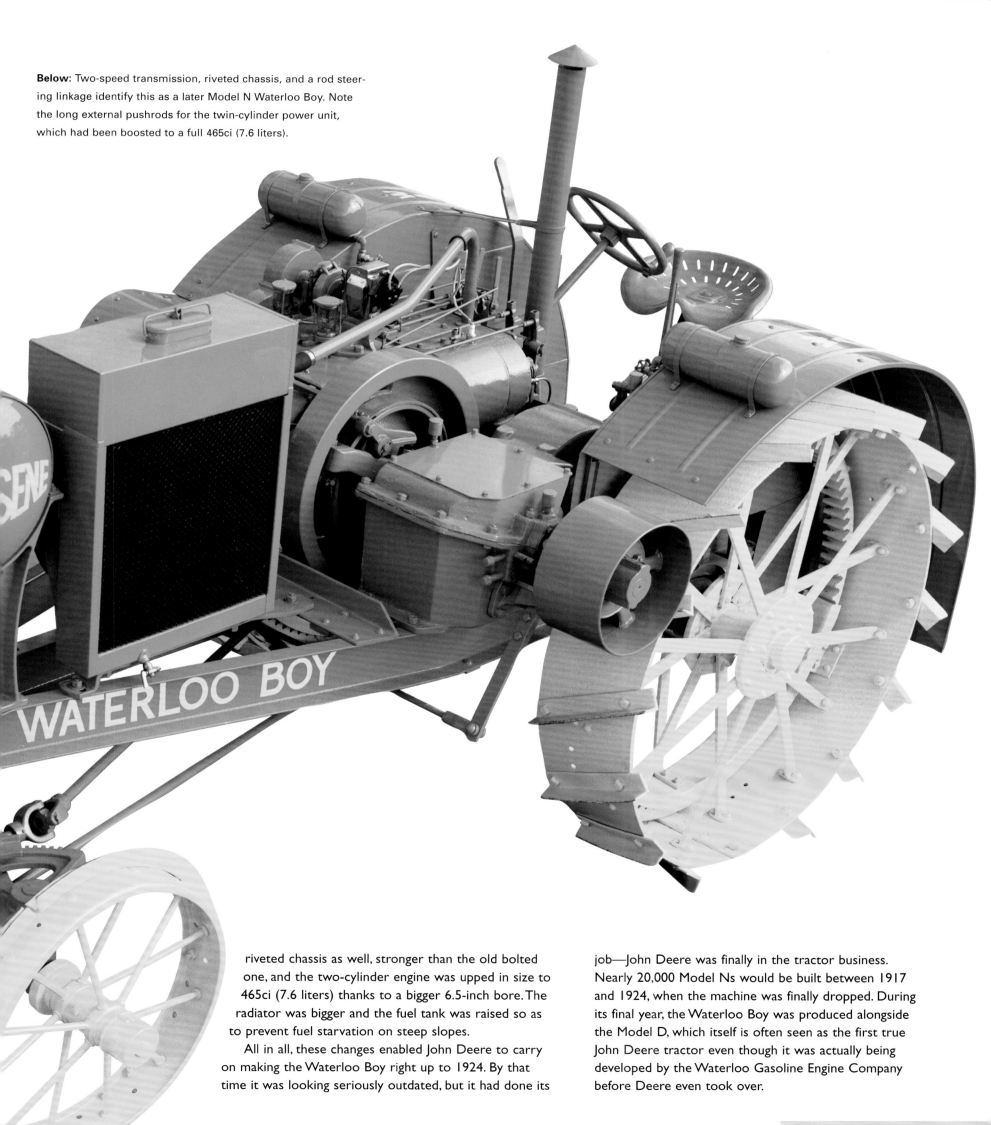

Below: Two-speed transmission, riveted chassis, and a rod steering linkage identify this as a later Model N Waterloo Boy. Note the long external pushrods for the twin-cylinder power unit, which had been boosted to a full 465ci (7.6 liters).

WATERLOO BOY

riveted chassis as well, stronger than the old bolted one, and the two-cylinder engine was upped in size to 465ci (7.6 liters) thanks to a bigger 6.5-inch bore. The radiator was bigger and the fuel tank was raised so as to prevent fuel starvation on steep slopes.

All in all, these changes enabled John Deere to carry on making the Waterloo Boy right up to 1924. By that time it was looking seriously outdated, but it had done its

job—John Deere was finally in the tractor business. Nearly 20,000 Model Ns would be built between 1917 and 1924, when the machine was finally dropped. During its final year, the Waterloo Boy was produced alongside the Model D, which itself is often seen as the first true John Deere tractor even though it was actually being developed by the Waterloo Gasoline Engine Company before Deere even took over.

Purchase of Waterloo Boy

The Waterloo Gasoline Company started business in 1893 in Iowa, growing from John Froelich's 1892 invention of the first gasoline engine-powered tractor that could move backward and forward. The company was producing engines by 1895. Production of the "Waterloo Boy" with its hopper-cooled open crank engine, began in 1914 and became a commercial success. Thus Waterloo became one of the most well-known tractor manufacturers along with Fairbanks Morse, Hercules, and International Harvester, and Waterloo engines were sold to many more companies besides.

In 1912 the John Deere company were starting to develop prototypes for their own tractors. In 1917 the "Dain" tractor went into production but only 100 were made because, although a superior product to many tractors, the cost of manufacture limited sales. John Deere were left with two choices: either continue to make tractors in the Dain design, or buy the Waterloo Gasoline Engine Company and use their well-established two cylinder Waterloo Boy Tractor.

In the *Waterloo Daily Courier* newspaper of April 1937 (the Waterloo company were based in Waterloo, Iowa), an interview with J.E. Johnson—the secretary and treasurer of the Waterloo Gasoline Engine Company in 1918— relates that "John Deere came to Waterloo because field tests showed 'Waterloo Boy [to be the] best tractor'." He goes on, "It happened that a representative of the John Deere organization was present and checking up on all demonstrations. When he had finished, he found that the Waterloo Boy had the best record." In 1918 John Deere

bought the Waterloo Gasoline Company and Johnson himself was a big part of the negotiations with John Deere over the sale.

After the purchase of the company the Dain design was discontinued. John Deere was happy with the two cylinder Waterloo Boy because as well as being successful it was a simple design and, relative to the Dain, inexpensive to build. Plus, they also now had more room to develop completely new tractors of their own (soon to be the Model D). The rest, as they say, is history...

Top: What John Deere bought—a flourishing factory and well-respected name.

Right: This is an early Waterloo Boy, with trademark transverse radiator and high-mounted fuel tank.

Left: This was the machine that took John Deere into the tractor business—the Waterloo Boy.

All-Wheel-Drive "Dain"

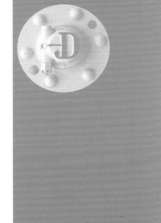
Well before John Deere bought up the Waterloo Boy, it had been experimenting with tractors of its own. A three-wheel prototype designed by C.H. Melvin was being tested as early as 1912, but it was Joseph Dain Snr. who would draw up Deere's first production machine.

This too was a three-wheeler, but there the resemblance with the Melvin tractor ended. The "Dain Deere," as it was sometimes known, was an advanced machine, arguably well ahead of its time, with all-wheel-drive, a four-cylinder engine, and shift on the go two-speed transmission. The first prototype was ready by February 1915 and looked promising. In one early test run it ploughed 80 acres with a three-furrow plough in Minnesota at a cost of just 59 cents per acre—and that included the driver's wages! It was sticky soil too, the farmer having previously used five horses to pull a single-furrow plough.

More prototypes soon followed and gear-drive transmission replaced the more primitive friction drive, while final drive was by chain. A more powerful McVicker-designed engine replaced the original Waukesha, and after two years of testing, it was thought that the "All-Wheel-Drive" John Deere had fully proved itself.

There was just one snag. The engine alone cost $200, and Deere estimated each tractor would cost around $600 to build, thanks to the complex transmission. Once dealer and manufacturer had taken their profit, the All-Wheel-Drive would be selling to the farmer for $1,200. This was a far cry from Joseph Dain's original aim of $700, and at that time the Waterloo Boy was selling for $850, so

the Dain-Deere would clearly be a premium product. However, the superior traction of all-wheel-drive, coupled with the time saved by its shift on the go transmission, led the company to go into production. It was reasoned that some farmers would be prepared to pay extra for these advantages.

In the event, Deere hedged its bets, only committing to a single batch of 100 Dain-Deeres. These were built in 1917, though they sold for a sky-high $1,700. The real death knell came early the following year, when John Deere took over the Waterloo Gasoline Engine Co.—this gave it a simple, proven, and popular tractor at around half the price. No more All-Wheel-Drives were made.

But the company didn't give up there. There were two more tractor projects, both of them three-wheel machines. The company was interested in the unit construction Wallis Cub, which had appeared in 1913, and Max Sklovsky designed a unit frame tractor for John Deere in 1915/16. It was a small machine with a four-cylinder Northway engine, but the outbreak of World War I prevented its development. Meanwhile, Walter Silver continued to develop motor cultivators for Deere right up to 1921. The unique steering system of one prototype guided it via steerable plough beams, making it excellent for row-crop cultivation. A tight-turning single rear wheel was used for headland turns.

Below: Four, not two, cylinders for the first production John Deere. But it was an expensive motor, inflating the Dain-Deere's price.

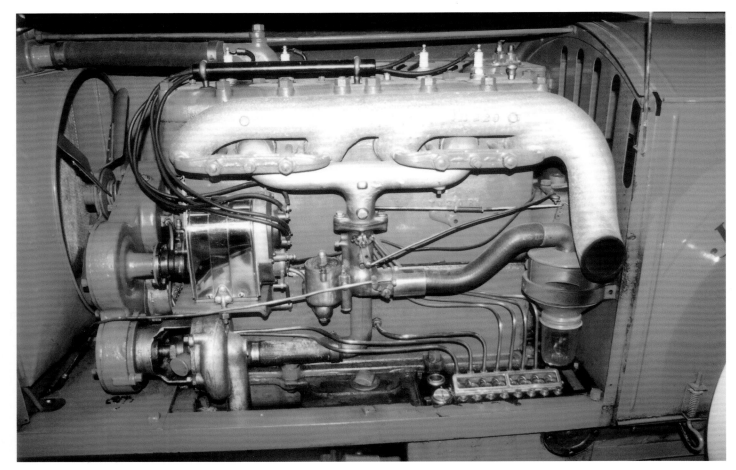

Above: Fully restored Dain Deere, with hard rubber covers on the three steel wheels.

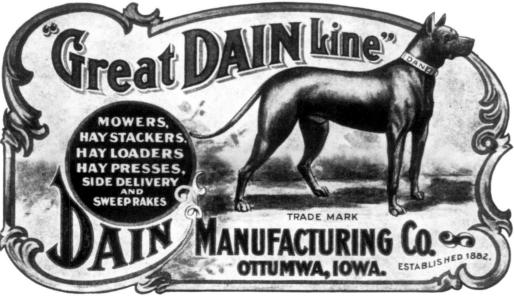

Left: Some in the company may have hoped that the "Great Dain" would open a new era for John Deere, but it was a false start.

Model D (unstyled)

SPECIFICATIONS

Model D (1923)

Engine type Twin-cylinder ohv, water-cooled

Fuel type Kerosene

Bore x stroke 6.5 x 7.0in

Capacity 464ci (7.6 liters)

Rated speed 800rpm

Carburetor Schebler DLT

TRANSMISSION

Transmission type Sliding-gear, chain final

Speeds 2F/1R

Speed range 2.5-3.25mph

DIMENSIONS

Factory weight 4,000lb

Tested weight n/a

Length 109in

Width 63in

Height 56in

Wheel size F 28 x 5

Wheel size R 46 x 12

Fuel tank (US gallons, main/aux) 8/2.5

Cooling capacity (US gallons) 13

PERFORMANCE

Power (at PTO) 37hp

Power (at drawbar) 28.5hp

Drawbar pull 4,462lb

Fuel efficiency 10.74hp/hr per gallon

Above: Belt work, powering threshers, and other farm machinery, was an essential part of early tractor duties. It reflected the tractor's origins as a portable stationary engine.

Is this the most successful John Deere of all time? Well, certainly the most enduring. The faithful Model D was in production for over 30 years, if you count both styled and unstyled versions—they were, after all, much the same tractor underneath.

Often thought of as the first "real" John Deere, the Model D was actually under development before Deere took over the Waterloo Company. Still, most of the work was done under the Deere umbrella, and (just as significant) this was the first twin-cylinder tractor to carry the John Deere badge. It also finalized the mechanical layout (twin horizontal cylinders) that the company would stay faithful to for decades. Slower revving and less smooth than multi-cylinder rivals it might be, but the Model D was simple, reliable and pulled like a cart horse from low speeds—this was what most farmers wanted, and "Johnny Popper" delivered.

But while it retained the same basic engine layout of the Waterloo Boy, the D was a great advance in other ways. Both two-speed transmission and chain final drive were enclosed in an oil bath, making for a longer, trouble-free life. The lack of a chassis saved weight and the whole tractor was neater and more compact than its predecessor. A contemporary John Deere brochure trumpeted the D's advantages: "GREATER SIMPLICITY. Exclusive, horizontal two-cylinder engine eliminates many unnecessary parts. Burns low-cost fuels successfully...

LOWER UPKEEP COST. Fewer adjustments required. Owner can make them himself because of greater simplicity and accessibility... HIGH-GRADE BEARING EQUIPMENT... SHOCK-PROOF, AUTOMOTIVE-TYPE STEERING... STRONG, ACCESSIBLE DRAWBAR... LONGER LIFE... " and so on.

The Model D managed to carry John Deere right through the Depression, though it was aided by lucrative export contracts to both Argentina and Soviet Russia, just when US tractor demand was at its lowest.

There were few major changes to the D in its first decade and a half, though a bigger 501ci (8.2 liter) engine arrived in 1927 (which took power up to 42hp, a 50% increase on the original) and a three-speed transmission seven years later, plus several minor improvements. There were also variations on the theme, ten Ds being fitted with crawler tracks and some equipped for orchard work. There was an industrial version too, the DI, though only 100 were made over six years. But these were sidelines; by 1953, when the D finally went out of production, over 160,000 mainstream models had been sold.

Below: John Deere's backbone. The Model D would become the company's longest serving model of all, seeing it right through the hard times of the 1920s and '30s.

Below: Early Model D— the solid flywheel dates it as a post-1925 machine.

LONG SERVING JOHN DEERES

Model	Years in Production
D	30 (1923-53)
A	18 (1934-52)
B	18 (1934-52)
G	16 (1937-56)
Waterloo Boy	10 (1914-24)

1926-1927

Model C

The entire US tractor industry got a wake-up call in 1924, when International Harvester unveiled the Farmall. Until then, tractors had either been low-powered lightweights for work in the fields or heavier, more powerful machines for belt work. The Farmall could do both—it was nimble enough for row-crops, yet powerful enough to do useful work driving other machinery.

John Deere—even the Waterloo Company—had been here before. For years, they had been experimenting with smaller tractors. Deere was field testing a lightweight two-plough machine as early as 1915. Designed by Max Sklovsky, it was a four-cylinder three-wheeler, and looked promising, but its relatively high-revving engine could not run on kerosene, so that was the end of that. Kerosene, which was much cheaper than higher-grade gasoline, was a must for any successful tractor in those days. A simpler, kerosene-friendly single-cylinder machine, designed to sell for just $600, would have solved that, but America's entry to Word War I put paid to that as well.

There were lightweight cultivators too, but at first these were hampered by lack of power, then by the rival International, which could cultivate two rows against the John Deere's one. The early '20s farming depression prevented the company from doing any further development work. But the arrival of the Farmall brought

a new impetus for the company, and 1926 saw a new John Deere, the Model C.

The C was more than just a miniaturized Model D, though it followed the familiar twin-cylinder layout, albeit with an L-head in place of overhead valves, and a smaller capacity of 312ci (5.1 liters)—power was 20hp, but the C had a three-speed transmission. Like the D, it was a four-wheeler, so it could cultivate three rows, and it was the first tractor to offer four power outlets: drawbar, belt, PTO, and mechanical lift. It also weighed 3,600lb, significantly less than either the D or the Waterloo Boy.

Five prototypes were built in 1926, with production starting the following year. So far so good, except that the C suffered from teething troubles, unlike its big brother, which was proving remarkably trouble-free, most probably because of its longer gestation period. The first batch of around 100 machines had to be recalled for modification, and only a further 23 Model C's were built in 1927. This was certainly a far cry from the D, which sold 1,000 in its first year alone.

In fact, the Model C didn't last very long at all. After barely a year in production it was dropped altogether and substantially reworked as the GP, which was far more successful. But at last John Deere had a tractor to compete with the all-conquering Farmall.

SPECIFICATIONS

Model C (1927)

Engine type Twin-cylinder L-head, water-cooled
Fuel type Kerosene
Bore x stroke 5.75 x 6.0in
Capacity 312ci (5.1 liters)
Rated speed 950rpm

TRANSMISSION
Transmission type Sliding gear
Speeds 3F/1R
Speed range 2.25-4.0mph

DIMENSIONS
Factory weight 3,600lb
Tested weight n/a
Length 112in
Width 60in
Height 55.5in
Wheel size F 24 x 6
Wheel size R 42.75 x 10
Fuel tank (US gallons, main/aux) 16/2
Cooling capacity (US gallons) 9

PERFORMANCE
Power (at PTO) 20hp
Power (at drawbar) n/a
Fuel efficiency n/a

Above: A beautifully restored John Deere C, in authentic setting. Smaller and lighter than the D, it took John Deere into a new market.

Right: It looks complex, but the C was supremely simple: L-head twin-cylinder engine and three-speed transmission.

Left: A brand new Model C, in one of John Deere's original publicity shots—not many C's would have stayed this pristine for long!

Model GP

SPECIFICATIONS

Model GP (1928)

Engine Type Twin-cylinder, water-cooled

Fuel type Kerosene

Bore x stroke 5.5 x 6.0in

Capacity 312ci (5.1 liters)

Rated speed 900rpm

TRANSMISSION

Transmission type Sliding gear

Speeds 3F/1R

Speed range 2.25-4.0mph

DIMENSIONS

Factory weight 4,265lb

Tested weight n/a

Length 112in

Width 60in

Height 55.5in

Wheel size F 24 x 6

Wheel size R 42.75 x 10

Fuel tank (main/aux) 16/2

Cooling capacity 9

PERFORMANCE

Power (at PTO) 25.0hp

Power (at drawbar) 17.2hp

Fuel efficiency 8.55hp/hr per gallon

If the Model C was something of a false start, then the GP was John Deere's all-purpose row-crop tractor for real. "John Deere General Purpose Farm Tractor," went the advert, "The Two-Plow Tractor that Plants and Cultivates Three Rows At a Time."

This was the Model C with all the bugs ironed out—there were no major changes, and the same 312ci (5.1 liter) L-head twin provided its reliable, slogging 20hp, but this time it was in for the long haul. Reflecting a fresh start, the name was changed from "C" to "GP." The story goes that when orders were being telephoned in to head office, there was frequent confusion between "C" and "D." Whether true or not, the "GP" tag better underlined the new tractor's General Purpose role. Like the International Farmall, it was designed to be nimble enough for row-crop work, yet powerful enough to drive a thresher or other non-powered machinery.

It worked well as a three-row machine, but there was a demand in the southern States for a two- or four-row tractor,

and John Deere responded with a tricycle version of the GP in 1928, complete with a rear track wide enough to straddle four rows. Like the C, this got off to a slow start, and only 72 were built in 1928/29.

It was followed by the more enduring GPWT (for Wide Tread) which ran through to 1932 and soon adopted a crossover steering linkage, in place of the side-steering arrangment. Another new linkage appeared in 1932, this time for overhead steering, with the steering box mounted just above and forward of the radiator. At the same time, the latest GPWT benefitted from a six-inch longer frame, raised operator's platform and larger 6-inch bore engine.

By this time, the standard GP also had the bigger motor, which displaced 339ci (5.5 liters) and boosted power to 25hp. This was fitted to the Series 3, 4, and 5 GPs, between 1930 and 1935, and lacked the water injection of its 5.5-inch bore predecessor. As with the

Below: This was John Deere's rival to the all-conquering Farmall: nimble enough for row-crop work, yet powerful enough to drive machinery.

Above: The model GP in action, demonstrating its ability to plant three rows at one pass.

Model D, there were a few variations on the GP theme, the most successful of which was an orchard-equipped GPO. A little over 700 were built over four years, and around 25 were converted to full crawler tracks by Lindemann.

John Deere's GP never really matched the phenomenal success of the Farmall, but it gave JD a vital toehold in the row-crop market.

MODEL RANGE

Model	Production Dates
GP Series 1 & 2	1928-30
GP Series 3, 4, & 5	1930-35
GPWT	1928-35

Model A (unstyled)

This is the tractor that effectively replaced the GP—the Model A—though confusingly both this and the smaller B often retained the "General Purpose" logo! Even as the GP was evolving into its ultimate WT form, it was obvious that the row-crop tractor in general was developing even faster—John Deere had some catching up to do.

Its answer, the Model A seen here, arrived in 1934.

This had been under development for two years, first as the FX and GX prototypes, later as the pre-production AA. Some of these had three-speed transmissions, but this was soon superseded by a four-speed. Already tractor transmissions were offering a wider choice of ratios—three just wasn't enough any more.

When it was launched, the new Model A also offered very good visibility from the operator's platform (useful for row-crop work, to keep an eye on what the attachments were doing) and a splined rear axle to allow adjustment of the rear tread. The latter was a big step

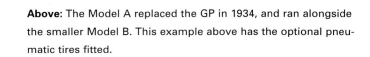

Above: The Model A replaced the GP in 1934, and ran alongside the smaller Model B. This example above has the optional pneumatic tires fitted.

forward, allowing the same tractor to work with different crop spacings, and would become an industry standard. Perhaps even more significant was the provision of an hydraulic lift. We usually credit Harry Ferguson and his famous three-point hitch as the first use of tractor hydraulics, and it was, but John Deere was there too. Of course, JD's version had none of the sophistication of the Ferguson hitch—it was an implement lift, pure and simple—but it did take some laborious work out of the mounting and demounting of heavy implements.

Confirming the success of the John Deere layout, the Model A stuck with twin horizontal cylinders, these measuring 5.5 x 6.0 inches for a capacity of 309ci (5.1 liters). However, it did adopt overhead valves in place of the GP's L-head, and produced the same power from fewer cubic inches.

The basic A was soon joined by the single-front-wheel AN and wide-front-axle AW, with high-clearance versions of both arriving in 1937. Meanwhile, the standard-tread became the AR and was joined by the AO (for orchards) in 1935. The latter adopted more streamlined bodywork the following year, with longer fenders and flush front

Above: Good visibility, the torquey, reliable twin-cylinder engine and a four-speed transmission made the A an adaptable row-crop machine.

MODEL RANGE

Model	Production Dates
A	1934-38
AN, AW	1935-38
ANH, AWH	1937-38
AR	1935-40
AOS	1936-40

grille to avoid snagging the branches. An industrial AI was less successful, while in 1941 the row-crop As benefitted from a 5.75-inch bore engine.

Model B (unstyled)

SPECIFICATIONS

Model B unstyled (1936)

Engine type Twin-cylinder ohv, water-cooled

Fuel type Kerosene

Bore x stroke 4.25 x 5.25in

Capacity 149ci (2.4 liters)

Rated speed 1,150pm

Carburettor Wheeler-Schebler DLTX

TRANSMISSION

Transmission type Sliding gear

Speeds 4F/1R

Speed range 2.3-6.25mph

DIMENSIONS

Factory weight 2,763lb

Tested weight 3,275lb

Length 120.5in

Width 85in

Height 56in

Tyre size F 22 x 3.25

Tyre size R 48 x 5.25

**Fuel tank
(US gallons, main/aux)**
12/1

**Cooling capacity
(US gallons)** 5.5

PERFORMANCE

Power (at PTO) 14.3hp

Power (at drawbar)
11.8hp

Fuel efficiency 10.28hp/hr per gallon

Until the advent of the Model C, it looked as if John Deere might be content to stay as a one-tractor company. After all the Waterloo Boy, and then the Model D, were both very successful, and Henry Ford had shown how a single model of tractor could cut costs to the bone and therefore win more customers.

But that was dispelled when the D was supplanted by the Model C/GP and underlined in the 1930s as the company announced a whole range of machines to slot in around the big D. It made sense, because as the market expanded and tractors got cheaper, there was a growing demand from smaller farmers, who didn't need and in any case couldn't afford a large tractor. So 1934 saw not just

the introduction of the Model A, but the little Model B, the smallest John Deere yet. It was designed to replace two horses, and be within reach of some of the smallest scale farmers in America.

The power unit was (you've guessed it) a miniaturized version of the Model A's, still overhead valve, but with cylinders measuring 4.25 x 5.25 inches for a capacity of just 149ci (2.4 liters). Almost of necessity, it ran at a faster 1,150rpm than its big brother, but still managed to produce a useful 16hp. And that power was put to good use, as the B was a real light weight, tipping the scales 900lb less (a 25% drop) than the Model A. Early Model Bs also had a shorter frame than the A, but this

Above: The Model B took John Deere into a new market for smaller tractors, complete with a 149ci overhead valve version of the twin-cylinder engine.

Above: Steel wheels on this Model B, with spade attachments to maximize grip. For roadwork, farmers would have to fit a smooth metal band over the spades—a tedious and time consuming job. Pneumatic rubber tires were the solution.

led to problems with changing implements between tractors, so it soon adopted the larger chassis.

As is often the case, the Model B was not much cheaper to make than the A (though of course farmers, like everyone else, expect a smaller product to be just that) but JD resisted the temptation to strip down the specification—the Model B still got a four-speed transmission and the same wide range of model variations as the A.

So there was a narrow-tread BN and wide-tread BW, with high-crop BNH and BWH. The BW40 was a special narrow axle tractor, using parts from the BO orchard machine. The BO had all the usual orchard changes: a lower stance, smoother bodywork, and independent rear-wheel brakes, and as with the AO, there was a Lindeman crawler conversion—nearly 1,700 of the latter were made up to 1946.

Left: Like every other row-crop tractor, the B came in a wide variety of forms. This is the wide tread BW with twin-wheel tricycle front-end. The latter remained a favorite of American farmers, but in Europe the standard tread was preferred.

Model Y/62/L unstyled

SPECIFICATIONS

Model L unstyled (1938)

Engine type Twin-cylinder, water-cooled

Fuel type Gasoline

Bore x stroke 3.25 x 4.0in

Capacity 57ci (934cc)

Rated speed 1,480rpm

Carburetor Marvel-Schebler

TRANSMISSION

Transmission type Sliding gear

Speeds 3F/1R

Speed range 2.0-6.5mph

DIMENSIONS

Factory weight 1,515lb

Tested weight 2,180lb

Length 111.25in

Width 79in

Height 52in

Tire size F 4.00 x 15

Tire size R 6.00 x 22

Fuel tank (US gallons) 6

Cooling capacity 2.5

PERFORMANCE

Power (at PTO) 10.4hp

Power (at drawbar) 7.1hp

Fuel efficiency 9.81hp/hr per gallon

Small it might be, but the miniature Model B was still too big for gardens or the horticultural industry. To suit the folk who worked in these environments, John Deere produced a very small number of mini-tractors, all of which eschewed the traditional horizontal Deere power unit for a vertical twin.

The company didn't have a suitable engine itself, nor a transmission, so the first batch of Model Y tractors used an off-the-shelf Novo motor mated to a Ford Model A transmission, with Ford steering gear and a welded frame. The Y was really an experimental tractor, as the 24 that left the Moline Wagon Works in 1936 were all recalled. But they were light enough (1,360lb) and cheap enough ($532.50) to fit the bill of a baby tractor.

Suitably encouraged, the company offered an uprated version the following year. It was still a single-plough machine, but its Hercules twin-cylinder engine produced 10.4hp at 1,550rpm. It was heavier than the Y, at 1,630lb, but the extra power was enough to make up the difference. The motor measured 57ci (934cc) with a bore

and stroke of 3.25 x 4.0 inches, and enabled the 62 (as it was now named) to pull a 12-inch plough, a corn cultivator, or disk harrow. One innovation was a slight offset to the operator station, allowing better visibility. There was a three-speed transmission allowing up to 6.5mph, and a PTO was optional.

In late 1937 the 62 became the Model L, though there were only minor differences between the two. It's easy to tell the difference at tractor shows though—the 62 has a large "JD" logo on its final drive housing and below the radiator, the Model L does not.

In total, 79 Model 62s were built, but nearly 4,000 Model Ls, and an updated, restyled L was available right up to 1946. Deere returned to the mini-tractor market in the early 1960s, and during the '80s and '90s the company would import Yanmar tractors from Japan to enable them to fill this gap in the range.

Above: That little twin was capable of hard work, and its compact dimensions afforded good visibility for implements such as the one seen here.

Above: It may have been dwarfed by larger machines, but the smallest Deere was a useful little tractor—note the simple tubular chassis.

Below: The American Dream (writ small)—a homestead, a plot of land, and a little John Deere to work it with...

Model G (unstyled)

Model G unstyled (1937)

Engine type Twin-cylinder ohv, water-cooled

Fuel type Kerosene

Bore x stroke 6.125 x 7.0in

Capacity 412ci (6.8 litres)

Rated speed 975rpm

TRANSMISSION

Transmission type Sliding gear

Speeds 4F/1R

Speed range 2.25-6.0mph

DIMENSIONS

Factory weight 4,400lb

Tested weight n/a

Length 135in

Width 84in

Height 61.5in

Tire size F 24 x 5

Tire size R 51.5 x 7

**Fuel tank
(US gallons, main/aux)** 17/1.5

**Cooling capacity
(US gallons)** 11

PERFORMANCE

Power (at PTO) 34.1hp

Power (at drawbar) 25.9hp

Fuel efficiency
10.7hp/hr per gallon

"The new John Deere Model G—for the Large Row-Crop Farm... Because of its abilty to pull large disk harrows, two-row corn pickers and four-row planters and cultivators, the Model G will especially appeal to the large-acreage corn grower... The Model G develops ample drawbar power to pull three 14-inch plow bottoms... On the belt, it will operate machines up to and including a 28-inch thresher."

So went the matter of fact brochure for Deere's Model G, introduced in 1937. Just like all the other JDs, this tractor provided a smaller variations on the Model D twin-cylinder theme, though in this case the G slotted in just underneath the big D. Its two cylinders measured 6.125 inches across and a stroke of 7 inches exactly. That made for a capacity of 412.5ci (6.8 liters) and a strong, reliable 34hp at its governed speed of 975rpm. According

to the compulsory test at the University of Nebraska, it could pull just over 4,000lb at the drawbar, at 2.37mph. It was the biggest row-crop on the market.

Like the smaller John Deeres, the G used a four-speed transmission, though in this case controlled by a single lever in a quadrant, not twin levers. According to the Nebraska test, this afforded speeds of 2.25, 3.25, 4.25, and 6.0mph. Steel wheels were standard, though of course as on just about every other mainstream tractor, pneumatic rubber tyres were an option, for extra speed and comfort. However, until it was restyled and updated in 1941, the big G came only in twin-front-wheel form—other Gs would follow.

The G also proved reliable, and no adjustments were needed to the Nebraska test tractor in 50 hours of running. There was just one problem with the early Model

Below: In 1937, this was the biggest row-crop tractor American farmers could buy, with 34hp from its 412ci motor.

Gs—the original radiator allowed them to run hot, and after the first 4,251 machines had rolled off the line, a bigger rad was fitted. End of problem. Nor did it seem to hurt the G's popularity, with over 60,000 built by the time production finally ended in 1953.

The big G came along at just the right time, as American farming was starting to claw its way out of the Depression, and farmers who could afford to were demanding bigger, more powerful tractors to give them a more competitive edge. This was the first inklings of the horsepower race that would dominate the industry throughout the 1950s, '60s, and '70s.

The Model G also had the effect of filling a large gap in the John Deere range. In the late 1930s, this now encompassed the Model L (10hp), Model B (16hp), Model A (25hp), G (34hp), and evergreen D (42hp).

Below: Below: For its first few years, the Model G was unstyled, bearing a strong family resemblance to the original Model D.

Below: The Model G in its element, busy ploughing a field. The transmission was four-speed, and the pneumatic tires, as shown here, were an extra-cost option.

Model A (styled)

SPECIFICATIONS

Model A styled (1947)

Engine type Twin-cylinder ohv, water-cooled

Fuel type Kerosene/Gasoline

Bore x stroke 5.5 x 6.75in

Capacity 321ci (5.3 liters)

Rated speed 975rpm

TRANSMISSION

Transmission type Sliding gear

Speeds 6F/1R

Speed range 2.5-13.0mph

DIMENSIONS

Factory weight 5,228lb

Tested weight n/a

Length 133in

Width 83in

Height 62.5in

Tire size F 24 x 4

Tire size R 50 x 6

Fuel tank (US gallons, main/aux) 14

Cooling capacity (US gallons) 6

PERFORMANCE

Power (at PTO) 35.8hp

Power (at drawbar) 26.7hp

Fuel efficiency 11.44hp/hr per gallon

John Deere tractors were not stylish. Tough, reliable, and stop at nothing, but not stylish. Yet despite the no-nonsense image and specification, the company where going to have to go out and buy a new suit of clothes.

This was the late 1930s—farming was well out of the Depression and America was well into a new age of streamlining and Art Deco. Cars and trucks took on the new look; fridges, radios… and even tractors. Rival manufacturers International Harvester hired the renowned designer Raymond Loewy to freshen up its tractors, and John Deere had no choice but to follow suit and hire their own personal design guru.

Legend has it that when John Deere's man turned up at the swish New York offices of stylist Henry Dreyfuss, he did so in a bucolic fur coat and straw hat. This so impressed the designer of the need for improvement that he took the job straight away!

The changes he made were only to sheet metal but they transformed the look of John Deeres, enclosing the radiator and fuel tank in a clean, squared-off hood. There were innumerable details as well, to make the latest JDs look all of a piece. They weren't rounded-off like the Loewy Internationals but Henry Dreyfuss' more severe sheet metal somehow suited John Deere's no-nonsense image.

At first, this was a styling exercise, pure and simple, with the new-look Model A remaining identical under the skin to the old one. But for 1941 the A got a significant update, in the form of an extra quarter-inch on the stroke, to give a new capacity of 321ci (5.3 liters) and almost 30hp at the belt. Not so

Above: Henry Dreyfuss' new sheet metal cleaned up the look of the Model A—now definitely a 1930s tractor, not a 1920s survivor.

Below: Not a Dreyfuss A, but the AO, streamlined for orchard work—the smooth metalwork was to prevent the tractor snagging on branches.

long ago, 30hp had been serious horsepower, now it was what one expected from a mid-range row-crop like the Model A. Just as significant was the six-speed transmission, just as three-speeds had been outmoded in the mid-1930s, now four wasn't enough any more.

As before, there was a whole selection of Model As to choose from, with narrow and wide axles, plus high-clearance versions. The AR and AO though, persevered with the pre-Dreyfuss styling and four-speed transmission until 1949, by which time the other As had been updated again, with a pressed steel frame and standard electric start and lighting. But they retained that clean, squared-off look that would be a John Deere feature up until 1960, when the New Generation took over. In no uncertain terms, Mr Dreyfuss had earned his fee.

Below: Orchard tractors like this AO always looked sleeker than their field-working brothers, but more by necessity than design.

Model B (styled)

SPECIFICATIONS

Model B styled (1941)

Engine type Twin-cylinder ohv, water-cooled

Fuel type Distillate

Bore x stroke 4.5in x 5.5in

Capacity 175ci (2.9 liters)

Rated speed 1,150rpm

TRANSMISSION

Transmission type Sliding gear

Speeds 6F/1R

Speed range 2.3-12.25mph

DIMENSIONS

Factory weight 3,900lb

Tested weight n/a

Length 132in

Width 86in

Height 60in

Tire size F 5.00 x 15

Tire size R 10 x 38

Fuel tank (US gallons) 12

Cooling capacity (US gallons) 7

PERFORMANCE

Power (at PTO) 19.7hp

Power (at drawbar) 16.5hp

Fuel efficiency 11.6hp/hr per gallon

When Henry Dreyfuss took on the challenging task of bringing John Deere styling up to date, the Model B formed the basis of his first work in 1937-38. As it turned out, the Dreyfuss-styled A and B were launched at the same time, and all the new sheet metal that worked so well on the A also featured on the smaller Model B. In fact, they looked identical, and unless you knew where to look for the small circular "A" or "B" badge just aft of the radiator there was no easy way to tell them apart.

But there was one difference that didn't show until one drove a restyled B. Unlike its big brother, this got a bigger engine to go with the new look, now with a bore and stroke of 4.5 x 5.5 inches for a capacity of 175ci (2.9 liters). Compared to the old 149ci motor, this gave a useful boost to 18.5hp (up from 16hp), which might not sound much, but JD beefed up the transmission to suit and fitted twelve-spline rear axles.

There were more updates for 1940, with the option of electric starting or lights—the former was especially welcome, as the 175ci twin-cylinder engine had been fitted with decompression valves to make hand cranking a little easier. There was a sloping dash to improve visibility and the hood was extended to hide the battery. The following year the B received the same six-speed transmission as the A, which according to Nebraska now permitted a heady 12.25mph on rubber tyres. The rubber incidentally, now a standard fitment on most US-made tractors, would soon disappear, as would the top two ratios of that six-speed gearbox, thanks to war shortages.

After World War II, the B shared the A's 1947 improvements—pressed steel frame, standard electric starting/lighting, enclosed flywheel, and improved seat. It also got another engine boost, this time to 190ci (3.1 liters), thanks to dimensions of 4.69 x 5.5 inches. Power, now at a rated 1,250rpm, was up to 23.5hp. The Model B contiued on in this form until 1952.

Most of its rivals might be on four-cylinders but that didn't seem to hurt the B, or hold back its regular updates. And of course, there was still a wide range of variants, with ultra-narrow, narrow, wide, and high-crop versions, though after 1947 the line-up was simplified to the standard B, narrow BN, and wide BW.

Above: The little Model B shared the same Henry Dreyfuss restyle as the A.

Above: The new-look B also benefited from a larger 175ci power unit (up from 149ci) to produce 18.5hp—decompression valves aided hand cranking.

Below: This is a single front-wheel tricycle front end Model B, with pneumatic rubber tires. Note spline adjustment of rear wheels.

Model L/LA (styled)

SPECIFICATIONS

Model LA (1941)

Engine type Twin-cylinder ohv, water-cooled

Fuel type Gasoline

Bore x stroke 3.5 x 4.0in

Capacity 77ci (1.25 litres)

Rated speed 1,850rpm

TRANSMISSION

Transmission type Sliding gear

Speeds 3F/1R

Speed range 2.5-9.0mph

DIMENSIONS

Factory weight 2,285lb

Tested weight n/a

Length 93in

Width 47in

Height 60in

Tyre size F 5.00 x 15

Tyre size R 9 x 24

Fuel tank (US gallons, main/aux)
8

Cooling capacity (US gallons)
2.5

PERFORMANCE

Power (at PTO) 14.3hp

Power (at drawbar)
10.6hp

Fuel efficiency 10.5hp/hr per gallon

Henry Dreyfuss, who had worked such magic on the A and B John Deere row-crops, had his work cut out doing the same for the sparse, dumpy little Model L. Deere's little utility tractor would never look dashing whatever was done to it, but Dreyfuss did manage to clean up the business end a little, with the rear end of the hood now curving down to the base of the steering column. There's also little doubt that the budget was more limited for this mini-tractor, which had to be built down to a price more than any other John Deere.

As well as the new styling, the Model L now had a John Deere-built engine of 10hp. Still a vertical twin, but with bore

and stroke of 3.25 x 4.0 inches to give a slightly greater displacement of 66ci (1.1 liters). It was joined in 1940 by the more powerful LA. The same engine was bored out to 3.5 inches for 77ci (1.25 liters) and rated at a relatively high 1,850rpm for an impressive 14hp. So impressive, that the little LA actually developed more drawbar pull than the bigger row-crop Model H in Nebraskan tests. With a solid-bar frame (instead of tubular steel on the plain L) and bigger 24-inch rear wheels, the LA weighed considerably more than the tractor it was based on, weighing in at 2,280lb. It could also reach 9mph on tarmac, in the tallest ratio of its three-speed transmission. A whole

Above: Henry Dreyfuss did his best with the dumpy Model L, and the result was neater and less utilitarian, though it still lacked the style of the bigger John Deeres.

range of options—rear PTO, electric start and adjustable front axle—could turn it into a well-equipped small tractor.

These mini-tractors were intended chiefly for horticultural work, but John Deere (perhaps influenced by the needs of wartime) also produced an industrial version, the LI, from 1942. "Before buying any tractor," advised the not impartial brochure, "consider this practical combination of features: Outstanding simplicity…Outstanding two-way economy…Easy to understand, easy to handle…Greater dependability…Longer life..Three forward speeds…Powerful for its size…Muffler, tool box, sickle carrier, oil gauge and high speed attachment…Electric starting and lighting extra…Speedy, strong, powerful, economical. A tractor built for all-round service." Who could resist the charms of a bright yellow LI?

However, all the miniature John Deeres were dropped in 1946, and it would be many years before the company tried selling another. And this time it would be a lawn tractor aimed at the private buyer.

Above: The "Johnny Popper," the nickname for all early John Deeres, and just as applicable to this little twin-cylinder L as the bigger ones. This is an early Model L, before it had the Dreyfuss styling treatment.

PRODUCTION DATES

Model	Production Dates
Model Y	1936
Model 62	1937
Model L unstyled	1937-38
Model L, LI styled	1938-46
Model LA	1941-46

1939-1953

Model D (styled)

When Henry Dreyfuss was brought in to freshen up John Deere tractors, the plan was always that he should transform the whole range. So while the new look debuted with the updated Models A and B in 1938, the little Model L and big D got the same treatment the following year, while the H (which filled the gap between LA and Model B, and appeared in January 1939) had the new styling from the start.

The Model D meanwhile, had become something of an institution. It was John Deere's only model for a short time, until it was joined by the GP, and it now found itself part of a 12-model range. It's also certain that this tough, reliable tractor was what helped the company survive when so many of its rivals fell by the wayside.

It had been gradually updated, notably with a three-speed transmission and a significant power boost, but was really much the same tractor as the machine introduced back in 1923, with strong links to the original Waterloo

Boy. But that didn't seem to matter to John Deere's faithful farming customers, who appreciated the Model D's staying power. It was the epitome of those Johnny Popper values: a low-revving two-cylinder engine mounted in a simple chassis, and many farmers carried on buying it in preference to four- and six-cylinder rivals.

But even John Deere accepted that its stalwart was starting to look outdated, even if many customers were happy with what went on under the sheet metal. So the D could not escape the Dreyfuss treatment, and the result was unveiled in 1939. There was no attempt to give it the same slimline look as the smaller A and B row-crop tractors. Instead, a eight-slat vertical grille hid the radiator, blending into a new hood. The front wheels had round spokes and the rears were 28-inch diameter, though these later changed to disc fronts and 30-inch rears. What didn't change was the engine, still the same 501ci

Below: Sticking with two cylinders didn't hurt John Deere too much in the 1930s, even while many rivals were moving to four or six cylinders.

SPECIFICATIONS

Model D styled (1940)

Engine type Twin-cylinder ohv, water-cooled

Fuel type Kerosene

Bore x stroke 6.75 x 7.0in

Capacity 501ci (8.2 liters)

Rated speed 900rpm

TRANSMISSION

Transmission type Sliding gear

Speeds 3F/1R

Speed range 3.0-5.25mph

DIMENSIONS

Factory weight 6,163

Tested weight 8,125lb

Length 130in

Width 66.5in

Height 61in

Tire size F 7.50 x 18

Tire size R 13.5 x 28

Fuel tank (US gallons, main/aux) 25/1.5

Cooling capacity (US gallons) 10

PERFORMANCE

Power (at PTO) 40.3hp

Power (at drawbar) 30.8hp

Fuel efficiency 10.1hp/hr per gallon

Above: For comparison, here is a Model D before the Henry Dreyfuss restyle, visibly almost identical to the 1923 original.

(8.2 liter) 6.75 x 7.0-inch horizontal twin, with water injection, 42hp, and a "mere" three speeds in its transmission.

So when John Deere announced that it was finally ending production of the Model D, after a 29-year run, there was an outcry. Another final batch had to be built to meet this last surge in demand. All of these end-of-line Model Ds were popularly known as "Streeters," as they were literally built up in the street, the one between the millroom and truck shop at Deere's Waterloo factory. The company owed the Model D a great deal, and its customers were not about to let it forget.

MODEL RANGE

Model	Production Dates
D Spoked Flywheel	1923-25
D 2-Speed	1926-33
DO	1926-33
D Crawler	1926-33
D 3-Speed	1934-39
DO	1934-39
DI	1934-39
D Styled	193?-52
D "Streeter"	1953

Model H

SPECIFICATIONS

Model H (1938)

Engine type Twin-cylinder ohv, water-cooled

Fuel type Distillate

Bore x stroke 3.56 x 5.0in

Capacity 91ci (1.5 liters)

Rated speed 1,400rpm

TRANSMISSION

Transmission type Sliding gear

Speeds 3F/1R

Speed range 2.5-5.75mph

DIMENSIONS

Factory weight 2,063lb

Tested weight 3,035lb

Length 111in

Width 79in

Height 52in

Tire size F4.00 x 15

Tire size R 7.50 x 32

Fuel tank (US gallons) main/aux 7.5/0.9

Cooling capacity (US gallons) 5.5

PERFORMANCE

Power (at PTO) 14.2hp

Power (at drawbar) 11.7hp

Fuel efficiency 11.7hp/hr per gallon

Back in the mid 1920s, John Deere had reacted to the success of International's Farmall with its own General Purpose tractor. The Farmall filled a demand so neatly that no mainstream manufacturer could afford to be without a rival, and soon the market was full of "general purpose" machines.

Deere found itself faced with the same dilemma in 1938, this time thanks to the runaway success of the new Model B from Allis-Chalmers. At less than $500, the latest machine from A-C offered the promise of a miniaturized full-size tractor at a very low price, next to which John Deere's L looked unsophisticated, while its own B was simply too big. There was definitely a demand for something between the two, as Allis proved by selling 11,000 Bs in its first year of production.

So in short order, John Deere designed, developed, and put into production the Model H which was built at the company's Waterloo factory. On paper it looked much closer to a full-size John Deere than the tiny model L. Most significant of all, it had the classic horizontal twin-cylinder engine, found

Above: The Model H was a truly miniaturized version of the big JDs, with the same twin-cylinder layout and sleek Henry Dreyfuss styling. It was a direct response to the Allis-Chalmers Model B.

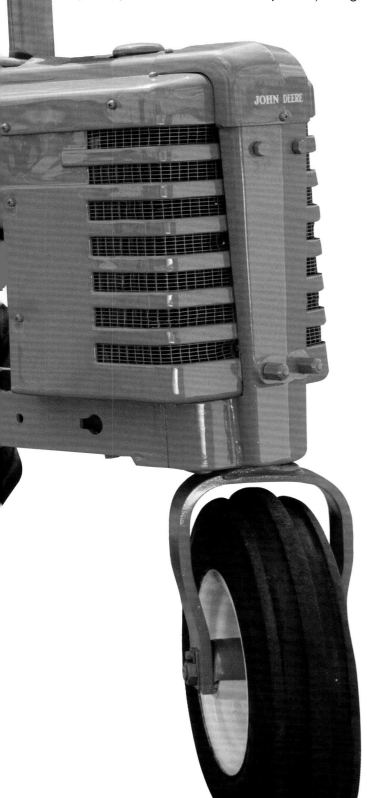

here in overhead valve form but smaller than ever before. Its capacity was 90.7ci (1.5 liters), with a bore and stroke of 3.56 x 5.0 inches. Rated at 1,400rpm, it produced 14.8hp. The only significant difference between this and the bigger Deere units (apart from size) was that the belt pulley was mounted on the end of the camshaft, and so rotated anti-clockwise.

Unlike full-size Deeres, with four- or soon to be six-speed transmissions, the H stuck with three speeds, (and the clutch was hand operated) though

it was possible to override the governor via a foot control. That allowed 1,800rpm instead of 1,400, and 7.5mph on the road.

But although the H had a simpler, cheaper specification than the bigger JDs, it looked just like them, having benefitted from the Dreyfuss style right from its introduction. To the untutored eye, it could be a top-spec Model A row-crop.

And although on paper the H had no more power than the utility LA, it was a genuine row-crop tractor, whereas the little LA was designed purely for horticulturalists. There was a whole string of variants too, to emphasize the H's adapatability: a single-front-wheel HN joined the standard H in 1940, with high-crop versions the year after.

John Deere sold 60,000 Model Hs before production was discontinued in 1947. This was not quite as many as the Allis-Chalmers sold over its much longer run, but remains a respectable volume for its day.

Below: Someone's pride and joy... smaller John Deeres are just as popular among restorers as the big ones.

Model G (styled)

SPECIFICATIONS

Model G styled (1947)

Engine type Twin-cylinder ohv, water-cooled

Fuel type Kerosene

Bore x stroke 6.125 x 7.0in

Capacity 412ci (6.8 liters)

Rated speed 975rpm

TRANSMISSION

Transmission type Sliding gear

Speeds 6F/1R

Speed range 2.5-12.5mph

DIMENSIONS

Factory weight 6,506lb

Tested weight n/a

Length 138in

Width 85in

Height 66in

Tire size F 6.00 x 16

Tire size R 12 x 38

Fuel tank (US gallons, main/aux) 17/1.5

Cooling capacity (US gallons) 13

PERFORMANCE

Power (at PTO) 36hp

Power (at drawbar) 27.1hp

Fuel efficiency 10.7hp/hr per gallon

By 1941, John Deere's big row-crop tractor, the 38hp Model G, was its only machine not to have been given the Henry Dreyfuss treatment—that sleek, squared-off look that had been such a success on those mid-range row-crop twins, the A and B. Not only that, but it still had just a four-speed transmission, hardly the thing for a flagship row-crop tractor to have.

John Deere decided to solve all this in one fell swoop, with a comprehensive revamp for the G, which had only been in production for four years. Four prototypes named GX were built and tested in 1941, and the result launched in early '42. In came the six-speed transmission (with a new Hi-Lo control lever) and in came the Dreyfuss styling.

Once again, it followed identical lines to those of the A and B, though

the new G could be identified as such, from its two side-by-side exhaust stacks—those on the smaller tractors were in-line. The engine went unchanged (being still relatively young, especially in John Deere terms) so wartime G buyers were offered the same 412.5ci (6.8 liter) horizontal twin with overhead valves. The G looked set for a new lease of life.

But there was a problem. One effect of America's entry into World War II was the introduction of stiff price controls, in an attempt to prevent inflation. Deere wanted to increase the price of the new G, to reflect all the extra equipment and retooling costs, but the Government refused permission. However, if the tractor was classed as a new model, then the company could charge whatever it liked. So the G rapidly became "GM" (the "M" for "modernised") and everyone was happy. The rule-bending nature of this decision was revealed when the wartime

Above: John Deere's biggest row-crop, the G, was finally given the Dreyfuss treatment in 1942, as the Wartime GM.

Above: Wartime price controls meant the restyled G was officially a new model. Whatever you called it the power came from the same 412ci power unit.

price controls were lifted and John Deere reverted immediately to plain "G." In any case, the tractor actually faced a two-year production hiatus between late 1942 and 1944 owing to the pressure of war work.

From 1947, the reborn Model G was now available with options already offered on the smaller John Deeres—there was a single-front-wheel GN and wide-front-axle GW, followed by a GH high-clearance. An electric starter and lights were now standard. Production ended in 1953, when many of John Deere's "letter" models were replaced by numbers.

MODEL RANGE

Model	Production Dates
G	1937-41
GM	1942-47
G, GN, WW, GH	1947-53

Model M

SPECIFICATIONS

Model M (1947)

Engine type Twin-cylinder side-valve, water-cooled

Fuel type Gasoline

Bore x stroke 4.0 x 4.0in

Capacity 100.5ci (1.6 liters)

Rated speed 1,650rpm

Carburetor Marvel-Schleber TMX

TRANSMISSION
Transmission type Sliding gear

Speeds 4F/1R

Speed range 1.6-10mph

DIMENSIONS
Factory weight 42,695lb

Tested weight n/a

Length 110in

Width 51in

Height 56in

Tire size F 5.00 x 15

Tire size R 9 x 24

Fuel tank (US gallons, main/aux) 10

Cooling capacity (US gallons) 3.5

PERFORMANCE
Power (at PTO) 19.5hp

Power (at drawbar) 14.7hp

Fuel efficiency 11.1hp/hr per gallon

By the late 1940s, John Deere's small tractor range was getting a little crowded, and confusing. First there was the Model L mini-tractor and its powered-up 14hp big brother, the LA. Second, the Model H, introduced just as World War II broke out, was bigger than the LA but no more powerful. Finally, the least elaborate Model B row-crop, the BR, was yet another alternative.

So the company decided to replace this multiplicity of models with just one, the M. It was actually under development while Allied troops were still battling their way through Europe, but it was three years before the Model 69 (as it was originally known) was finally unveiled.

Actually, it wasn't just rationalization that convinced JD to launch another new tractor.

Like every tractor manufacturer, John Deere was under threat from the Ford 9N and Ferguson T20, both of them with Harry Ferguson's revolutionary hydraulic three-point hitch. The advantages of the Ferguson system were legion: it made for quick and easy implement hitching; it improved traction through automatic draft control; and it was safer, preventing the tractor from turning over backwards.

The Model M didn't have that (Ferguson's patents were cast-iron) but it did have John Deere's own Quik-

Left: The Model M replaced a whole group of small tractors in the John Deere range—the L/LA, H and (to a certain extent) the B.

Tatch hitching system and Touch-O-Matic hydraulics. Neither was as sophisticated as the Ferguson system, but they did add a measure of convenience. To go with the Quik-Tatch were more than twenty implements to suit the tractor. In fact, the little M was quite well equipped, with electric start and a PTO standard—electric lights and a belt pulley were optional.

Although the new tractor was developed at the Moline Wagon Works, John Deere built a brand new factory, at Dubuque, Iowa, to assemble the M. From the start it had Dreyfuss styling and variations soon followed a year or so after the original launch. There was a twin-front-wheel MT, single-front-wheel MTN, wide-front-axle MTW, and an MC crawler, which replaced the BO-L, plus a shorter, lower industrial MI. All were powered by a 100.5 ci (1.6 liter) vertical twin, producing just over 20hp at the PTO, and married to a four-speed transmission. The agricultural Ms were produced to 1952, with the MI hanging on for another three years.

Above: The M was John Deere's response to the success of the new breed of utility tractors from Ford and Ferguson, though it lacked the famous three-point hitch.

Model R (1st Diesel)

Diesel is ideal for tractors. Its power characteristics—low rev lugging ability—and its fuel efficiency are two very good reasons why almost every tractor made in the world today is diesel powered.

Half a century ago things were very different, and despite diesel engines having been around for many years, few American tractors (crawlers apart) used them. John Deere had been experimenting with diesel in the 1930s, when International was already offering its multi-fuel WD-40 tractor, which could run on either gasoline or diesel. It took JD another decade to perfect its own diesel, but when it did, it was a winner.

The early prototypes had been

diesel versions of the venerable Model D, but when it arrived, the Model R had been designed from scratch. There was clearly no question of John Deere taking the four- or six-cylinder route with its first diesel, and the R stuck with the familiar horizontal twin-cylinder layout. It was huge—each piston measured 5.75 inches across and ran up and down a stroke of eight inches, the crankshaft spinning at a leisurely 1,000rpm. At 416ci (6.8

SPECIFICATIONS

Model R (1949)

Engine type Twin-cylinder ohv, water-cooled

Fuel type Diesel

Bore x stroke 5.75 x 8.0in

Capacity 416ci (6.8 liters)

Rated speed 1,000rpm

TRANSMISSION

Transmission type Sliding gear

Speeds 5F/1R

Speed range 2.1-11.5mph

DIMENSIONS

Factory weight 7,603lb

Tested weight n/a

Length 147in

Width 79.5in

Height 78in

Tire size F7.50 x 18

Tire size R14 x 34

Fuel tank (US gallons, main/aux) 22

Cooling capacity (US gallons) 13.6

PERFORMANCE

Power (at PTO) 48.6hp

Power (at drawbar) 34.5hp

Fuel efficiency 17.6hp/hr per gallons

liters) this was not John Deere's biggest-ever engine, but it was its most powerful, at 48.6hp at the belt and over 34hp at the drawbar.

Not only that, but it was staggeringly efficient. Tested at Nebraska in April 1949, it achieved a fuel economy of 17.35hp/hr per gallon, setting a new record. This was unbroken, incidentally, until the R's replacement was tested three years later, and in the next 35 years only sixteen tractors surpassed it—that was out of over 1,000 machines tested! In fact, it began something of a John Deere tradition for fuel efficiency—the later diesel-engined 70, 720, and 1650 also scored very highly.

Another notable feature of the big diesel was that its big, high compression cylinders made hand cranking impossible. Even a standard electric start would have had difficulty, so the R was equipped with a little twin-cylinder donkey engine (running on gasoline) whose job it was to preheat the big diesel before a cold start was attempted. A 24-volt electric start was used later.

Efficient and reliable with a good strong pull—no wonder John Deere sold over 20,000 Model Rs.

Left: Four-square, powerful, and always ready for work—that was the John Deere R. It was also highly fuel-efficient, setting a new fuel economy record at the University of Nebraska. Later John Deere diesels continued the tradition.

Model 50

SPECIFICATIONS

John Deere 50 (1952)

Engine type Twin-cylinder ohv, water-cooled

Fuel type Gasoline

Bore x stroke 4.7 x 5.5in

Capacity 190ci (3.1 liters)

Rated speed 1,250rpm

TRANSMISSION

Transmission type Sliding gear

Speeds 6F/1R

Speed range 1.5-10mph

DIMENSIONS

Factory weight 4,855lb

Tested weight 5,433lb

Length 133in

Width 87in

Height 60in

Tire size F 5.50 x 16

Tire size R 11 x 38

Fuel tank (US gallons, main/aux) 15.5

Cooling capacity (US gallons) 7

PERFORMANCE

Power (at PTO) 28.9hp

Power (at drawbar) 20.9hp

Torque 184lb ft

Fuel efficiency 11.8hp/hr per gallon

A new era dawned for John Deere in 1952... that is to say a new era in its model designation system. Actually, the changes were far more involved than that, and to reinforce the point, all John Deere tractors were renamed in the space of a few years: the Model B became the 50, A the 60, G the 70, and finally the R became the 80.

Engine apart, the 50 was a virtually new tractor, with a cast frame in place of the pressed steel item used previously. One significant new feature was Powr-Trol, a live PTO driving through a second gear on the crankshaft ahead of the main clutch. Pioneered by the Canadian manufacturer Cockshutt, it allowed the continued operation of powered machinery, even while the tractor was stopped with the clutch disengaged—

before that, if the tractor stopped, the combine stopped as well, not exactly helpful!

Another convenience feature was a new method of adjusting the rear tread. Setting the rear wheels on splined axles had seemed like a great step forward, twenty years before, and it was, but it still required a lot of hard labor, as the wheels had to be bashed along the splines by sledgehammer. On the new John Deeres, the wheels were moved via a rack and pinion, and fixed by means of a keyway on a tapered sleeve. That definitely saved a few sweaty hours and strained muscles.

To underline the new features (there was more power from a revised engine as well) the 50 received similar styling to the Model R, copying its attractive wrap-around grille, the first modification to the Henry Dreyfuss styling that had served so well since 1938. All the 50s were row-crop machines, with the usual single-front-wheel, twin-front-wheel, and conventional front axle

Above: A new number for a new era. The 50 replaced the Model B, and included a new cast frame, a live PTO, and rack and pinion wheel adjustment.

Above: Slim and neat John Deere 50—the company was starting to think about an all-new replacement, but in the meantime the old twins kept on selling.

options. The Model 50 had another significant update in 1953, which included a proper three-point hydraulic hitch that followed along Ferguson lines—as the Ferguson patents ran out, most tractor makers were quick to build their own version of the famous hitch. And in 1955, the year before the 50 was replaced, an LPG (liquid petroleum gas) option was added. For a decade or so, this was a popular choice—it wasn't as economical as diesel, but was a cheaper fuel than liquid gasoline.

SPECIFICATIONS: MODEL 50 (1952-56)

Engine	Twin-cylinder, ohv
Capacity	321ci (5.3 liters)
Power	38hp
Weight	5,300lb (2,406kg)

1952-1956

Model 60

SPECIFICATIONS

John Deere 60 (1952)

Engine type Twin-cylinder ohv, water-cooled

Fuel type Gasoline

Bore x stroke 5.5 x 6.75in

Capacity 321ci (5.3 liters)

Rated speed 975rpm

TRANSMISSION
Transmission type Sliding gear

Speeds 6F/1R

Speed range 1.5-11.0mph

DIMENSIONS
Factory weight 5,911lb

Tested weight 7,405lb

Tire size F 6.00 x 16

Tire size R 12 x 38

PERFORMANCE
Power (at PTO) 38.6hp

Power (at drawbar) 28.0hp

Torque 251lb ft

Fuel efficiency 11.6hp/hr per gallon

Models A and B seemed destined to be offered almost as a matched pair. They had been launched in the same year, looked identical and were the same physical size, once the little B adopted the longer frame of the A. So it was with the 50 and 60, though the 60, which replaced the A, actually beat the 50 to market by four months.

It benefitted from the same changes. Styling was along the lines of the Model R—the wrap-around grille somehow made the tractor look bigger and more substantial—and there was a one-piece hood which also hid the air intake, and a right-hand muffler which could easily be removed thanks to an external fitting. The frame was now cast instead of in pressed steel. There was also the new rack and pinion rear tread adjusting system, which made life easier for the hard working farmhand.

That wasn't the end of the list. There was an independent live PTO—it cost extra, but was the latest in tractor technology, enabling powered machinery to carry on working while the tractor was stopped. John Deere's

Above: Model 60 buyers enjoyed 28% more belt power than they had with its predecessor, the Model A.

version of the three-point hitch was compatible with 24 different implements. Farmers also wanted more power, so both 60 and 50 were given hot and cold manifolds, duplex carburation, and a cyclonic fuel intake.

Behind the marketing speak, there were genuine power increases. According to the Nebraska tests, the new 60 was 28% more powerful (at the belt) than the A it replaced, and the 50 was 23% punchier than the B. There was a belt-driven water pump as well, to improve cooling, plus other internal improvements. Otherwise, the 60 continued with the same 321ci (5.3 liter) horizontal twin as before.

Longer control levers made life easier for the driver too, with less bending and stretching needed—the science of improving operator comfort might not be called "ergonomics" yet, but that was what it was.

There was a wider range of 60s than 50s. As well as the usual row-crop options (single-front-wheel, twin-front-wheel, standard axle), buyers could choose orchard and high-clearance versions as well.

Left: The 60 carried on where the Model A left off as John Deere's mid-sized row crop tractor.

Model 40

Below: The 40 was John Deere's smallest tractor in the early 1950s: basically a restyled Model M with 15% more power.

SPECIFICATIONS

John Deere 40 (1953)

Engine type Twin-cylinder ohv, water-cooled

Fuel type Gasoline

Bore x stroke 4.0 x 4.0in

Capacity 101ci (1.6 liters)

Rated speed 1,850rpm

TRANSMISSION

Transmission type Sliding gear

Speeds 4F/1R

Speed range 1.6-12.0mph

DIMENSIONS

Factory weight 3,219lb

Tested weight 4,569lb

Length 131in

Width 89in

Height 59in

Tire size F 5.00 x 15

Tire size R 9 x 34

Fuel tank (US gallons, main/aux) 10.5

Cooling capacity (US gallons) 3.5

PERFORMANCE

Power (at PTO) 23.5hp

Power (at drawbar) 17.4hp

Fuel efficiency 11.3hp/hr per gallon

With the little L/LA and H gone, the Model M was the smallest tractor offered by John Deere in the late 1940s and early 1950s. It too was subject to the new numbering regime, and in 1953 was relaunched as the 40 series, slotting in neatly under the 50 and 60. For the orderly of mind, the numbers made a lot more sense than the old letters—it took some mental gymnastics to accept that a Model G was the biggest tractor in the range, the L the smallest, with the A and B somewhere in between!

For the renamed 40, this also entailed many of the changes that benefitted its larger siblings: more power, more convenience features, and new styling. Once again, the 40's styling took elements of the Model R—notably the slatted wrap-around grille, though in this case a solid metal divide ran down the centre. More significant was the 15% power increase (to 25hp at the belt)—there was

no duplex carburation, as on the bigger 50 and 60, just an increase in rated speed by 200rpm to 1,850rpm.

The ex-Model M power unit clearly had potential, but otherwise it was unchanged, a vertical twin-cylinder engine of 101ci (1.6 liters) of square bore and stroke dimensions (4.0 inches each). There was no diesel option yet, and in fact one wouldn't be available with the smallest John Deere until the very end of the 1950s, just before the New Generation of tractors swept all before them. Until then, the choice was just between all-fuel and pure gasoline.

The small Deere was expected to adapt itself to many different jobs, so several versions were available: standard S, utility U (a style popularized by the Ford 9N and small Ferguson), tricycle T (single-front-wheel), Hi-crop H, and crawler C. A year after the 40's introduction, a high-clearance V was added, and in 1955 the Two-Row Utility W. There was also a wide-front-axle option as well.

The University of Nebraska tested the standard 40 in September 1953 and recorded speeds of 1.6-, 2.1-, 4.25-, and 12mph for its four-speed transmission—the top ratio was clearly meant for road work only. In 74 hours of testing, no repairs or adjustments were needed and working the tractor at a maximum belt load yielded a fuel efficiency of 11.16hp/hr per gallon—not bad for the standards of the time—but it puts the diesel Model R's 17.35hp/hr into perspective.

Above: John Deere made combine harvesters too, with production starting in 1927.

Above: Recognize that radiator grille? It was the Model R influence. A large, comfortable seat indicates a greater consideration for the driver.

Model 70

SPECIFICATIONS

John Deere 70 (1954)

Engine type Twin-cylinder ohv, water-cooled

Fuel type Diesel

Bore x stroke 6.125 x 6.4in

Capacity 376ci (6.1 liters)

Rated speed 1,125rpm

TRANSMISSION
Transmission type Sliding gear

Speeds 6F/1R

Speed range
2.5-12.5mph

DIMENSIONS
Factory weight
7,137lb

Tested weight
9,017lb

Tire size F 6.00 x 16

Tire size R 13 x 38

PERFORMANCE
Power (at PTO) 50.4hp

Power (at drawbar) 25.9hp

Drawbar pull 6,189lb

Fuel efficiency
17.7hp/hr per gallon

Above: The 70 used a V4 donkey motor to start its big diesel—electric starting was later an option.

John Deere's first diesel, the Model R, had been a huge success, setting new fuel economy records and educating American farmers into the benefits of diesel power. As a result, thousands were sold. So it was inevitable that diesel power would trickle down to the smaller John Deeres.

But it didn't happen overnight. The 70 Diesel—JD's first diesel row-crop machine—didn't appear until 1953, four years after the R was launched. In fact, apart from the little GM-powered 435, introduced as a gap filler just a year before the 1960 New Generation took over, and the big 80, no other 1950s John Deere were diesel powered.

For the 70, Deere adopted the same tack as with the Model R, introducing a diesel version of the horizontal flat-twin. Although very close in capacity to the Model R (412ci against 416ci) the 70's engine was quite different, with a shorter 7-inch stroke and a larger 6.125-inch bore to compensate. Some sources give the engine smaller dimensions and 376ci (6.1 liters)—it's likely that the 70 started out with the smaller engine and later progressed to the larger.

Despite these dimensions, the 412 was rated at a slightly lower speed than the 416—975rpm versus 1,000—and power was almost identical, at 51.5hp at the belt, just slightly up on the R. Another difference was the option of electric starting and (if that wasn't specified) the use of a V4 donkey motor instead of the R's flat-twin. So never let it be said that John Deere never fitted a four-cylinder engine to one of its pre-1960 tractors—they did!

The 70 was actually available with four fuel options: diesel, gasoline, all-fuel, and LPG. This was the beginning of an era when all four would fight for supremecy in the US tractor market—diesel would eventually come out the winner, but it would take another 20 years.

In the meantime, Nebraska tested all four power options on the John Deere 70 during 1954. With hindsight, the results were predictable: the diesel scored top in belt horsepower, low-gear drawbar pull (6,189lb for the record) and fuel efficiency. Of the other three, LPG scored the best torque, power, and pull, but at the cost of abysmal efficiency (9.56hp/hr per gallon, against the diesel's 17.74).

SPECIFICATIONS: MODEL 70 GASOLINE

Engine	Twin-cylinder, ohv
Bore x stroke	5.9 x 7.0in
Rated speed	975rpm
Drawbar power	44.2hp
Transmission	6-Speed
Speeds	2.5-12.5mph
Weight	6,035lb

Right: Chunky and ready to work, the 70 came with four fuel options: diesel, gasoline, all-fuel, and LPG.

Below: Despite the success of the Model R, it took John Deere four years to come up with its next diesel.

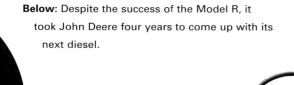

1955-1956

Model 80

SPECIFICATIONS

John Deere 80 (1954)

Engine type Twin-cylinder ohv, water-cooled

Fuel type Diesel

Bore x stroke 6.1 x 8.0in

Capacity 472ci (7.7 liters)

Rated speed 1,125rpm

TRANSMISSION
Transmission type Sliding gear

Speeds 6F/1R

Speed range 2.5-12.25mph

DIMENSIONS
Factory weight 8,511lb

Tested weight 11,495lb

Tire size F 7.50 x 18

Tire size R 15 x 34

PERFORMANCE
Power (at PTO) 65.3hp

Power (at drawbar) 46.8hp

Torque 424lb ft

Drawbar pull 7,394lb

Fuel efficiency 17.8hp/hr per gallon

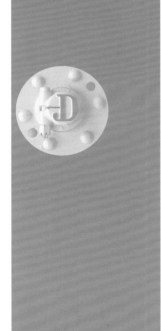

The Model R had started out as John Deere's biggest, most powerful tractor, but now it looked like being eclipsed by the new 70 Diesel. While the rest of the range was being renewed and numbered, the big R soldiered on—it was hardly outdated, having debuted only a few years previously but the tractor power race was gathering speed and JD couldn't afford to be left behind.

So in 1955 the R was the last tractor to get its number—80 in this case—along with a substantial boost in both power and capacity. By increasing both bore and stroke (the latter by a full inch) JD's biggest twin-cylinder motor ever came out at 472ci, or 7.7 liters. Rated speed was notched up from 1,000 (for the R) to 1,125rpm, and the end result was more than 30% extra belt horsepower, to 67.6—drawbar power was up to 61.8hp, making the 80 one of the most powerful tractors on the market. The torque figure was impressive too—424lb ft at 768rpm. And being a John Deere diesel, the 80 was highly efficient as well, at 17.58hp/hr per gallon.

Deere's method of starting these huge twin-cylinder diesels had always been intriguing, and in place of the Model R's tiny two-cylinder donkey engine, 80 adopted the gasoline V4 introduced with the 70 diesel. This was actually the Waterloo factory's first attempt at a four-

cylinder engine, and it worked very well. With a capacity of 18.85ci (just over 300cc) it could run straight up to 5,500rpm, and its exhaust was routed in such a way that it prewarmed the big diesel to make that first start of the day possible.

It was a mechanically complex system, and although it worked, John Deere later offered the option of a heavy-duty 24-volt system, beefy enough to allow direct electric starting of those two big cylinders, even on the frostiest mornings.

There were other advances for the 80, notably a six-speed transmission, which Nebraska reckoned to give a speed range of 2.5 to 12.25mph. A three-main-bearing crankshaft, live PTO, and twin hydraulic valves for two remote cylinders were other new features.

Many of the numbered John Deeres now had a power steering option as well. As it turned out, the 80 Diesel was short-lived, being updated as the 820 in 1956.

Below: More cubic inches (now 472) and a higher rated speed produced an extra 30% more belt horsepower over the Model R this 80 replaced.

Above: Restored 80 at an agricultural show in Britain. Big by the standards of its time, but the 80 would be dwarfed by some modern day tractors.

Top: Model 80 put to an unconventional use. The tractor was powerful enough to cope with a high capacity front attachment.

420/430

SPECIFICATIONS

John Deere 420S (1956)

Engine type Twin-cylinder ohv, water-cooled

Fuel type All-Fuel

Bore x stroke 4.25 x 4.0in

Capacity 113ci (1.8 liters)

Rated speed 1,850rpm

TRANSMISSION

Transmission type Sliding gear

Speeds 4F/1R

Speed range 1.6-12.0mph

DIMENSIONS

Factory weight 3,019lb

Tested weight 4,311lb

Tire size F 5.00 x 15

Tire size R 10 x 24

PERFORMANCE

Power (at PTO) 22.7hp

Power (at drawbar) 17.1hp

Drawbar pull 1,482lb

Fuel efficiency 9.98hp/hr per gallon

This was the beginning of the end for the twin-cylinder John Deeres, a line which stretched right back to the first Waterloo Boy of 1914. A 46-year run was good enough in anyone's terms, but Deere had decided to finally let go of the classic Johnny Popper. The New Generation was under development but in the meantime the old twins would have to persevere for just a few more years.

That was the thinking that lay behind the final 20 and 30 series, which introduced some useful improvements and updates, just to keep the twins acceptable, and the changes were applied across the entire range.

The 40 series was the first to benefit, as the 420 in 1955. The model line-up was unchanged: standard S, utility U, tricycle T , Hi-crop H, crawler C, high-clearance V, and

Two-Row Utility W. They all looked very similar to the original 40 (apart from the discreet badges) that is at least until June 1956, when the color scheme changed from the original all-green to the classic green with yellow stripe that has become so familiar ever since.

More significant was extra power from the twin, thanks to an extra quarter-inch on the bore, which took its capacity up to 114ci (1.9 liters). It now gave just over 29hp at the belt, up from 25hp on the 40. That was on gasoline, and the All-Fuel version made that 23.5hp at 1,850rpm. An LPG option was added later, but there was

Below: The 420/430 was a holding operation, keeping the little twin-cylinder tractor fresh for a few more years before the New Generation took over.

no diesel engine for the agricultural 420s. Industrial users though, could specify a GM two-stroke diesel in the wheeled 440 or crawler 440C.

Otherwise, the new 420 could also be had with a five-speed transmission, a live PTO, and dual Touch-O-Matic hydraulics. Availability of the three-point hitch was extended to the crawlers as well, while a Special Utility was added to the range in 1957.

For its last two years, the 420 became the 430, which in truth was really just a restyle to give John Deere's smallest row-crop twin one last lease of life. Of these, the RCU (Row Crop Utility) was the best seller, and the several T (tricycle) versions did well too—crawlers always sold in smaller numbers than their wheeled counterparts.

Above: This was the final incarnation of the small twin-cylinder John Deere, and there were hardly any differences between the 420 and the 430.

Below: That familiar yellow strip denotes a June '56-on 420—prior to that, John Deeres were all-green. Power was up to 29hp at the PTO and capacity to 114ci (1.9 liters).

320/330

There was just one snag with the 420. All the new options and that bigger engine made it more expensive, and it was supposed to be John Deere's lead-in model. There were still plenty of farmers who wanted nothing more than a cheap, basic tractor, but not to worry, JD had the answer ready and waiting.

It simply carried on making the 40 series, but rebadged it as the 320, to act as the new entry-level machine beneath the 420. Power still came from the "square" dimensioned horizontal twin, with a four-inch bore and four-inch stroke. That produced 20.5hp at the PTO, at the rated 1,650rpm, from its 101ci (1.6 liters). The transmission was still four-speed (unlike the 420, there was no five-speed option) and the whole tractor weighed 2,605lb (1,203kg) in gasoline form. It was so little changed from the 40, that no new test at Nebraska was deemed necessary.

There were two basic models, the standard 320S and utility 320U, the latter being designed along the lines of

the successful Ferguson T20 and Ford 9N—in other words, a lower seating position than the pure row-crop tractors but with all-round capabilities. John Deere customers still preferred the 320S though, which was the better style of the two. Later a 320V was added to the range. Also known as the Southern Special, it had larger rear tires and a higher front axle, for greater crop clearance.

As with the 430, there was a final update in 1958, to take the cheapest John Deere through its last 18 months of production. Restyled, with a more rounded hood, the 330 also received a slanted dash and steering wheel. But not many were made, as by now the smaller twin-cylinder John Deeres were seriously showing their age against the four-cylinder opposition.

Below: The 320/330 made a useful utility tractor, but the twin-cylinder John Deere was nearing the end of its life.

Above: If the 420 (an updated, uprated 40) was too expensive, John Deere would still sell you a 40, albeit rebadged as the 320.

Right: One option on the 320/330 was an offset front axle, to allow better visibility of mid-mounted implements.

520/530

Those smaller John Deeres—the 320/330 and 420/430—were all assembled at the Dubuque factory, the new plant Deere had built in 1945 specifically to make the new small Model M. But all the bigger Deeres were always built at Waterloo, where tractors bearing the John Deere badge had rolled off the line for decades, and would for decades more.

The 520, which replaced the 50 series in 1956, was the smallest of these. Like every other 20 series tractor (except the entry-level 320) the 520 was given a power boost to go with its new badge and the classic green and yellow color scheme. Thanks to an increase in rated speed from 1,250rpm to 1,325rpm, and an increase in compression ratio from 6.1:1 to 7.1:1, power was up to 26.6 belt hp for the All-Fuel version, and a much healthier 36.1 belt hp on the gasoline model.

According to Nebraska figures, the gasoline version was a 25% increase on the old model, so the company was certainly doing its best to keep up with the multi-cylinder opposition—only now, close to the end of the twin-cylinder engine's life, was it starting to look like a handicap.

Not that this bothered the hardcore of loyal John Deere customers and, in fact, even in that Nebraska test, the 520 still performed well. It showed up the traditional Deere twin-cylinder strengths, notably good torque from low revs. The test machine was found to produce 105% of its rated torque at 85% of the rated speed, again at 65% rpm, and again at 60%. The tractor could pull nearly 4,700lb in low gear (at 1.37mph) and economy peaked at 12.74hp/hr per gallon. Gear speeds in the six-ratio transmission were 1.5, 2.5, 3.5, 4.5, 5.8, and 10mph. The test tractor gave no trouble and needed no adjustments in over 38 hours of running time.

When the 530 was announced in 1959, it was not to

Below: The 520/530 was the smallest tractor built at John Deere's Waterloo plant in the 1950s. The four-cylinder 1010 replaced it in 1960.

Above: The 520, the penultimate incarnation of the Waterloo-built 50. That in turn could trace its roots back to the Model B of 1934.

herald any major mechanical changes, and as with the smaller tractors, the 30 series denoted a restyle only.

However, there were new flat-top fenders with twin headlights, sway blocks for the three-point hitch and the option of Quick-Change rear-wheel treads. Otherwise, the end was nigh for a tractor that had originally started out as the Model B, 25 years previously.

SERIAL NUMBERS

Model	520	530
Production dates	1956-58	1958-60
First Serial number	5200000	5300000
Final Serial number	5213189	5309814

620/630

SPECIFICATIONS

John Deere 620 (1956)

Engine type Twin-cylinder ohv, water-cooled

Fuel type Gasoline

Bore x stroke 5.5 x 6.4in

Capacity 303ci (4.9 liters)

Rated speed 1,125rpm

TRANSMISSION

Transmission type Sliding gear

Speeds 6F/1R

Speed range 1.5-11.5mph

DIMENSIONS

Factory weight 7,015lb

Tested weight 8,655lb

Tire size F 6.00 x 15

Tire size R 13.6 x 38

PERFORMANCE

Power (at PTO) 44.3hp

Power (at drawbar) 33.6hp

Fuel efficiency 12.5hp/hr per gallon

Like every other 20 Series John Deere update of the mid 1950s (except for the big 820), the mid-range 620 benefited from extra power. But while its smaller siblings extracted the power boost from extra cubic inches, the 620's horizontal twin was actually smaller than the unit which it replaced!

John Deere engineers managed this apparently impossible feat by upping the rated speed from 975rpm to 1,125rpm, while the spark plugs were moved from the block to the cylinder-head. Not that this new rated speed was especially high—the bigger 720 and 820 were rated the same, while the smaller 420 and 520 ran faster. But the 620 would certainly have been happy at higher revs, as the engineers had shortened the stroke from 6.75 to 6.375 inches, cutting capacity to 303ci (5.0 liters) from 321ci (5.3 liters).

The result was a useful 15% power increase (based on Nebraska tests of the gasoline versions) to 44.25hp at the belt, and the whole tractor was strengthened to cope. Despite the extra horses, Nebraska also found that the 620 was more fuel efficient than its predecessor. The 620 recorded 12.52hp/hr per gallon at maximum belt load, compared to 11.61.

As well as the revised engine, the 620 enjoyed the same changes as the 520. The new Category 2 three-point hitch now had load and depth sensing (Harry Ferguson's patents had run out, to the benefit of the entire tractor industry) plus a sway block. Custom Powr-Trol—the up to date hydraulic system with three separate circuits—featured, as did the Quick-Change rear-wheel tread. Power steering was standard now, as it was on the 520—this had been an option since 1954, and John Deere was first to offer this as a built-in factory option on a row-crop tractor. Another new feature was the Float-Ride seat, to improve comfort.

There was still no diesel 620 though, and power options remained gasoline, LPG, or All-Fuel. The latter, which used a lower 4.78:1 compression than the others, was tested by Nebraska in November 1956. It might accept cheaper fuel, but was substantially down on power (to a maximum 32.9hp at the belt) and was less fuel-efficient into the bargain. In 1959, all the 620s were restyled for their final year as 630s, though the orchard model soldiered on in its old guise—sales didn't justify the new tin work.

Above: For 1956, 60 became 620, and acquired that famous yellow stripe.

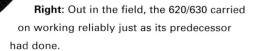

Above: The 620 hard at work baling in the 1950s. This powered-up tractor had plenty of horsepower to run a baler
and the laden trailer as well.

Right: Out in the field, the 620/630 carried
on working reliably just as its predecessor
had done.

720/730

SPECIFICATIONS

John Deere 720 (1956)

Engine type Twin-cylinder ohv, water-cooled

Fuel type Gasoline

Bore x stroke 6.0 x 6.4in

Capacity 361ci (5.9 liters)

Rated speed 1,125rpm

TRANSMISSION

Transmission type Sliding gear

Speeds 6F/1R

Speed range 1.5-11.5mph

DIMENSIONS

Factory weight 6,065lb

Tested weight 7,505lb

Tire size F 6.00 x 15

Tire size R 15.5 x 38

PERFORMANCE

Power (at PTO) 55.1hp

Power (at drawbar) 40.4hp

Drawbar pull 6,647lb

Fuel efficiency 12.2hp/hr per gallon

Remember the Model G, introduced back in 1937 as John Deere's new big row-crop machine? This was the latest incarnation of that tractor, now with a diesel option. In between times, the G had been steadily updated, getting the Henry Dreyfuss styling treatment in 1941, plus a six-speed transmission and the "GM" tag (to avoid that wartime restriction on price increases). It became the 70 Series 12 years later, complete with an ultra-economical diesel option that set a new record at Nebraska.

Now this long-running row-crop tractor was in its final few years, which for 1956 meant the same 20 series update as all the other Deere tractors. This brought substantially more power, underlining the fact that John Deere was having to work hard to keep its twin-cylinder tractors up with the power race. In the long-term of course there was no way that the traditional JD twins could keep up with four- and six-cylinder rivals, but until the Waterloo factory had perfected the long-awaited New Generation, the twins would have to cope as best they could.

Not that it looked too difficult for Waterloo engineers

Below: Nearly all the 20 series updated John Deeres of the '50s got a power increase—20% in the case of the 720 gasoline.

Above: A 730 on a demonstration run. Many restored tractors now give working demonstrations, rather than sitting as static museum pieces.

to squeeze more power out of the traditional layout. According to Nebraska, the 720 gasoline produced 55.1hp at maximum belt load, up 20% on the equivalent 70. Like the smaller 620, it proved slightly more efficient than its predecessor on that test, at 12ihp/hr per gallon, but again, as with the 620, Deere engineers managed this in fewer cubic inches. The new tractor had a shorter six-inch stroke but an extra 0.375 inches on the bore—the result was a capacity of 361ci (5.9 liters) down from 413ci (6.8 liters).

The diesel of course, was substantially different, with bore and stroke of 6.125 x 6.375 inches for a capacity of 376ci (6.2 liters) which was unchanged from the 70. It still used the V4 donkey gasoline engine to start up, though later 720 diesels also offered an optional electrical system. Both incidentally, were also slightly

more powerful than the gasoline equivalent, with 56.7hp at the belt.

In 1959, the 730 brought a final restyle but few mechanical changes, except for the option (from March of that year) of a 1,000rpm PTO, which was offered on all the Waterloo-built tractors. The following year, the 730 ceased production, along with all the other twin-cylinder John Deeres. Or did it? In 1961, the tooling was shipped to Rosario in Argentina, whence it rolled off the lines right up until 1970.

820/830

SPECIFICATIONS

John Deere 820 (1957)

Engine type Twin-cylinder ohv, water-cooled

Fuel type Diesel

Bore x stroke 6.1 x 8.0in

Capacity 472ci (7.9 liters)

Rated speed 1,125rpm

TRANSMISSION

Transmission type Sliding gear

Speeds 6F/1R

Speed range 2.5-12.25mph

DIMENSIONS

Factory weight 8,729lb

Tested weight 11,995lb

Tire size F 7.50 x 18

Tire size R 15 x 34

PERFORMANCE

Power (at PTO) 72.8hp

Power (at drawbar) 53hp

Drawbar pull 8,667lb

Fuel efficiency 17.3hp/hr per gallon

In 1956, John Deere's big diesel, the 80, became the 820. But unlike the smaller tractors, it did not come with a power increase. This was rectified in July the following year, with the giant twin-cylinder diesel was persuaded up to 75.6hp at the belt, and almost 70 at the drawbar.

There were no major changes to produce these power figures—capacity remained at 472ci (7.7 liters) and rated speed 1,125rpm—but they made the 820 one of the most powerful tractors you could buy. It was strong enough to pull a six-bottom plough, which gives a good idea of the extra power available. More recently Don Dufner has linked three 830s together, and these proved capable of hauling implements designed for modern 200hp+ four-wheel-drive tractors.

But of course, being a John Deere diesel, the 820 was efficient as well as powerful. Not quite as economical as the short-stroke 720 diesel, whose new record in University of Nebraska tests of 17.97hp/hr per gallon would stand until 1983. In fact, at 17.28hp/hr per gallon it was less efficient than its immediate predecessor, the 80, as well as the original Model R—John Deere's first diesel which wowed the agricultural world in 1949 with its sheer efficiency. By the way, the 720's record was broken by, you guessed it, another John Deere, the 1650.

All this economical power had applications beyond the farm, and there was an industrial version of the later 830 as well, the 830I. This built in an offset driving

Below: With a power boost in 1957, to over 75hp, the big 820/830 remained one of the most powerful tractors available—not bad for a mere two cylinders.

position, which all owed the fitment of a Hancock 8 cu yd (6 cu m) self-loading scraper, and was introduced in October 1958.

Meanwhile, all 820s became 830s, and as with all the other 30 series John Deeres for 1959, this was little more than a cosmetic exercise to keep the old twin-cylinder tractors selling for their final 18 months of life. There were some substantive changes as well though, such as a sloping steering wheel and easier to use instrument panel. Power-adjustable rear wheels became an option, while a cab was available as an extra from 1957. These were all sensible changes to keep the twins attractive but they were marginal at best. The real revolution was about to happen.

Above: An after market cab fitted to an 830. In the late 1950s, few owners chose to pay extra for a cab, which were in any case less effective than the later factory-fitted items.

Above: If you couldn't afford or didn't want a cab, the next best thing was a giant umbrella to keep the sun off!

435

In early 1959, John Deere's New Generation was only 18 months away from its official launch. A short enough time, you might think, for the twin-cylinder Johnny Poppers to last, given their regular updates with new options, more power, and improved ergonomics.

Well perhaps, but with one exception. Farmers in both North America and Europe were turning to diesel power in a big way—it made a lot of sense, given the good lugging power and excellent economy of compression ignition. And not just for big tractors either. John Deere and its rivals were now under intense competition from Ferguson and Ford, both of whom offered small utility tractors with a diesel option. The New Generation might be only 18 months away, but John Deere couldn't wait that long—it needed a small diesel tractor in early 1959.

With the new four-cylinder engines under development,

the only option was to buy a motor in, so that's what they did. Thus the little 435 (and the 440 Industrial version) was powered by a GM supercharged two-stroke diesel, here in vertical twin-cylinder form, of 106ci (1.7 liters). It was an unusual power plant for a tractor, of different power characteristics to a conventional diesel, but a precedent had been set by Oliver, which had been offering GM two-strokes in its bigger tractors since 1955, and continued to do so into the 1960s.

As it was, the 435 provided about the same amount of power as the gasoline 430 whose chassis it shared (just under 33hp at the PTO) but more torque. It was quite high revving by tractor standards, rated at 1,850rpm, but was still more economical than the 430, at 14.49hp/hr per gallon at max PTO horsepower. The five-speed transmission gave a speed range of just under 2mph to 13.5mph and the little tractor could pull just over 2,000lb at the drawbar.

Above: Apart from the biggest machines, this was the only diesel-powered John Deere on offer during the '50s, the 435.

There was an industrial version too, the 440, which was available with John Deere's own gasoline vertical twin as well as the GM diesel. This came in both wheeled and track form, the latter still offering the choice of gasoline or diesel engines mated to a five-speed transmission. But in the final analysis, the 435 was merely a stop gap tractor, and the real action in 1959 was taking place over at the nearly new Waterloo research and engineering center. There, John Deere engineers were putting the finishing touches to something quite revolutionary.

SPECIFICATIONS: 430 GASOLINE

Engine	Twin-cylinder, ohv
Bore x stroke	4.25 x 4.0in
Rated speed	1,850rpm
Drawbar power	27.1hp
Transmission	4-Speed
Speeds	1.6-12.0mph
Weight	2,750lb

Right: If there was a gasoline equivalent of the 435, this 330 and the 430 did the job.

Right Below: The 435 was the agricultural version, but the industrial 440 was also available in gasoline form.

8010

SPECIFICATIONS

John Deere 8010 (1959)

Engine type Six-cylinder two-stroke, water-cooled

Fuel type Diesel

Bore x stroke 4.5 x 5.0in

Capacity 425ci (6.9 liters)

Rated speed 2,100rpm

TRANSMISSION
Transmission type Sliding gear

Speeds 9F/1R

Speed range 2.0-18.0mph

DIMENSIONS
Factory weight 20,700lb

Tested weight 24,860lb

Length 235in

Width 96in

Height 98in

Tire size F n/a

Tire size R n/a

Fuel tank (US gallons, main/aux) n/a

Cooling capacity (US gallons) n/a

PERFORMANCE
Power (at PTO) 215hp (claimed)

Power (at drawbar) 150hp (est)

Fuel efficiency n/a

In 1959 at Marshalltown, Iowa, John Deere made its last presentation of new-model twin-cylinder tractors. But there was something else. It also showed the giant 8010, the first modern four-wheel-drive super-tractor to be offered by a mainstream manufacturer. With the combination of four-wheel-drive, an articulated chassis, and over 200hp, this set-up bore an uncanny resemblance to the modern super-tractor, meaninng JD's latest offering was far ahead of its time.

Perhaps, with hindsight, it was just too far ahead. The brochure certainly had to hard-sell on why such a large, expensive tractor was worth buying. "With the 10-ton, four-wheel-drive 8010, a fleet owner can retire up to three 6-plow tractors and their operators. 8010 fuel savings are outstanding too—in recent tests an 8010 with a 31-foot tool carrier covered 19 acres an hour at a cost of only 6 cents per acre. Here is truly power for profit."

Apart from the few big four-wheel-drive tractors being sold by the Steiger brothers in Dakota, there was nothing else quite like the 8010 at the time. Certainly most farmers would never have seen anything so powerful at work in the field. At that first Marshalltown demonstration, they saw it hook up to a massive eight-bottom plow, which it proceeded to pull with almost contemptuous ease.

Below: Ahead of its time. John Deere's 8010 had many of the features of a modern super-tractor: four-wheel-drive, an articulated chassis, and, of course, lots of power.

It was innovative too, with features that wouldn't appear on mainstream tractors for years to come. There were air brakes, two separate hydraulic circuits, and an hydraulic clutch. The air system could be used to inflate the tractor's own tires, while the front wheels could be shifted in and out to reduce on-road wear. There were convenience features as well: when the headlights were on, so too were courtesy lights illuminating the steps and toolbox, while most of the grease points were grouped together.

The 8010 offered more than three times the power of a contemporary big row crop or wheatlands tractor. This came courtesy of a supercharged GM two-stroke diesel, with six cylinders and 215hp. Other parts were bought in too, like the nine-speed truck transmission. It was thought that sales wouldn't be high enough to warrant designing, tooling up and making parts in-house. They weren't wrong—despite the futuristic specifications, few 8010s were sold.

Right: Bigger and more capable than any tractor from a mainstream manufacturer, but the 8010 was too expensive, and reliability problems sealed its fate.

Below: At early demonstrations farmers were amazed by the 8010's ability to pull an eight-bottom plough, well within its limits. But however impressed they appeared to be, few actually bought one.

New Generation (1960)

August 30th, 1960: groups of well-dressed men with nervous smiles wait outside the Memorial auditorium in Dallas, Texas. It's a clear, bright morning and already the heat is becoming oppressive. But there's excitement in the air—something big is about to happen. Bus after bus pulls up outside, the passengers pile out and stream into the auditorium. There are over 6,000 of them: John Deere dealers, managers, financiers, and guests. They're all here to witness the first public showing of John Deere's New Generation of Power, the all-new four- and six-cylinder tractors that will replace the entire range of Johnny Popper twins overnight.

For the company, this launch was vital. The launch day itself—never mind the design and development of the New Generation—had taken two years planning and cost over $1.2 million. No less than 162 planes flew in guests from all over the world; over 6,000 hotel rooms had been booked; at the gala barbecue that evening, 5,000lb of beef was roasted, together with over 3,000 chickens, and 1,800lb of ribs. All day the guests were entertained with ice shows, films, and shown the 136 new tractors and 223 implements. It all ended with a massive firework display. Why had John

Above: John Deere's New Generation was a terrific gamble— attempting to replace the entire tractor line-up in one fell swoop was no mean feat.

Deere gone to so much trouble? Why had they dropped the well-proven twin-cylinder tractors in favor of these new ones?

Plenty of people did ask those questions, and with good reason. After all, John Deere was a comfortable second place in the USA, behind International Harvester. It had thousands of loyal customers and made good profits. Why change a winning formula? Why risk all of this with a brand new range?

To find answers, we have to go back in time a decade or more from Dallas. As World War II ended, John Deere found itself the only major tractor manufacturer still relying on a twin-cylinder engine—International Harvester,

Case, Allis-Chalmers, and the rest had all moved up to fours and sixes. For years, Deere had stuck doggedly to its twin-cylinder philosophy: simplicity, reliability, and low speed slogging power.

But times were changing. Farmers wanted more outright power now and the faithful twin, for all its good points, was nearing the top of its development curve. But still a debate raged on within the company. Some argued that an all-new design was the only way forward, and a four-cylinder mock-up had been built as early as 1950, but others thought John Deere should stick to what it knew. It was president Charles Deere Wiman (great grandson by marriage of the original John Deere) who made the ultimate decision in 1953. The company would design an all-new range of four- and six-cylinder tractors. And they wouldn't settle for second place any more—the aim was to snatch market leadership from International.

It was an audacious and far sighted move. Far sighted, because the new tractors would be seven years in the making; audacious because if they failed, the whole scheme could conceivably bring about the demise of the company. Oh, and never before had the company attempted such an ambitious new model programme—it simply had to succeed.

Work began straight away. Amid great secrecy, the design team moved into an empty supermarket (well away from the main factory) and later into the company's new Project Engineering Center just outside the city. Lots of work was done on V-engines—a range of V4s, V6s, and V8s—but these compromised visibility and were rejected. A flat-four was also considered…and dropped. Likewise, many different transmission types made it into to metal, before being scrapped.

In the end, the New Generation took shape as a range of tractors with relatively conventional in-line four- and six-cylinder engines, but as part of an innovative, thoroughly modern package. Since practically everything about the New Generation was, well, new, it all had to be exhaustively tested. The new tractors were hooked up to dynamometers, locked into cold rooms, and driven through mud baths. John Deere owned a test farm as well, where the machines were rigorously field tested.

Of course, outside the company, few people realized this was going on—the prototypes were painted red (instead of tell-tale JD green) to put nosey parkers off the scent. And the secrecy worked, for when the covers were finally pulled off in Dallas on that August morning, few people knew what to expect.

After seven years of work, countless hours of testing, and millions of dollars spent, the New Generation was finally ready to go on sale. The big question was, would John Deere's big gamble pay off?

1010/2010

SPECIFICATIONS

John Deere 2010 (1961)

Engine type Four-cylinder ohv, water-cooled

Fuel type Diesel

Bore x stroke 3.88 x 3.50in

Capacity 165ci (2.7 liters)

Rated speed 2,500rpm

TRANSMISSION

Transmission type Syncro Range

Speeds 8F/3R

Speed range 2.7-19.3mph

DIMENSIONS

Factory weight 5,120lb

Tested weight 6,392lb

Wheelbase 87in

Tire size F 6.00 x 16

Tire size R 13.6 x 28

Fuel tank (US gallons, main/aux) n/a

Cooling capacity (US gallons) n/a

PERFORMANCE

Power (at PTO) 46.7hp

Power (at drawbar) 39.3hp

Drawbar pull 3,399lb

Fuel efficiency 12.78hp/hr per gallon

"The New Generation of Power is a full line of tractors, all with the new variable-speed 4- or 6-cylinder engines. Take your choice of 35hp 1010, 45hp 2010, 55hp 3010 or 80hp 4010." (John Deere advertisement, 1960.)

Those four new tractors, unveiled at Dallas, really divided into three groups. The mid-range 3010 and six-cylinder 4010 were all-new, with lots of strong new features. The 2010 shared some of those features, but also shared an engine with the little 1010. The latter turned out to

be, if not the runt of the litter, then at least the most trouble. John Deere's new four-cylinder engine was a sleeve-and-deck design, with all four cylinder sleeves cast as one unit. This turned out to be less than reliable, especially on the 145ci (2.4 liter) diesel, which suffered from warpage in the manufacturing process—that in turn allowed O-rings sealing the bottom of the sleeves to fail, allowing coolant or oil into the cylinders. Otherwise, the 1010 used many proven 430 parts, with a simple five-speed transmission.

The 2010 was closer to the bigger tractors in specification. It used a bigger version of the sleeve and deck engine (145ci/2.4

Above: Baby of the New Generation, though the 1010 really shared many parts with the old 430.

Above: The 1010 was something of a false start—not until 1965 did John Deere have a truly modern small tractor.

liter gasoline, 165ci/2.7 liter diesel) and was available with the New Generation Syncro-Range transmission, which gave eight forward and three reverse speeds. In terms of tractor technology, this was a big step forward from the old five-speed. The 2010 also offered an LPG option, where the 1010 came as gas or diesel only.

Both tractors came in a multiplicity of models. The 1010 could be ordered as a Row-Crop Utility (by far the most popular), a Single-Row Crop low-profile Utility, Orchard, and Agricultural Crawler. There were variations on each of these, adding up to ten models in all. The 2010 came as Row Crop, Row Crop Utility, Hi-Crop, and Agricultural.

But despite the wide choice, neither of the smaller New Generation machines had the success of their Big Brothers: John Deere sold fewer than 18,000 1010s in six years of production. The truth was that neither of these tractors were true New Generation machines in the way that the 3010 and 4010 really were. According to tractor historian (and ex-John Deere dealer) Don MacMillan, the 1010 was little more than a four-cylinder version of the old 430 twin. In late 1965, John Deere replaced them both with truly modern small tractors.

3010/4010

SPECIFICATIONS

John Deere 4010 (1960)

Engine type Twin-cylinder ohv, water-cooled

Fuel type Diesel

Bore x stroke 4.12 x 4.75in

Capacity 381ci (6.2 liters)

Rated speed 2,200rpm

TRANSMISSION

Transmission type Syncro Range

Speeds 8F/3R

Speed range 1.5-14.5mph (gasoline model)

DIMENSIONS

Factory weight 7,445lb

Tested weight 9,775lb

Wheelbase 96in

Tire size F 6.00 x 16

Tire size R 15.5 x 38

Fuel tank (US gallons, main/aux) n/a

Cooling capacity (US gallons) n/a

PERFORMANCE

Power (at PTO) 84.0hp

Power (at drawbar) 71.9hp

Drawbar pull 4,737lb

Fuel efficiency 14.97hp/hr per gallon

If the 1010/2010 were aspirant New Generation tractors, then the four-cylinder 3010 and six-cylinder 4010 were the real thing. They really were all-new, and allowed John Deere to leap ahead of the opposition. Overnight, the company was transformed from safe, conservative tractor maker, to a technological leader.

Take the hydraulic system. At the time, most tractor hydraulic pumps delivered around 1,000psi. The Deere New Generation could pump 20 gallons a minute at twice that pressure. This allowed one central pump to provide hydraulic power for a multiplicity of functions. Power steering, power brakes, and power rockshaft as well as the three-point hitch with lower-link draft sensing, plus there were three independent "live" circuits. The pump shared its oil with that of the transmission and differential, which made servicing simpler, and its power drain when the system wasn't in use was a scant 1.5hp, so it was effiicient as well.

This alone was enough to put the 3010/4010 ahead of the opposition, but they also had the eight-speed Syncro-Range transmission as standard, with three reverse speeds. The new engines scored too, the 3010 powered by a 201ci (3.3 liter) gasoline/LPG or 254ci (4.1 liter) diesel, with 55hp at the PTO. But JD's new row-crop flagship was the 80hp 4010, using the same bore and stroke as the 3010, but in six-cylinder motors: 301ci (4.9 liter) gasoline/LPG or 381ci (6.2 liter) diesel.

There was some doubt that John Deere loyalists, weened on the slogging, slow-revving twin, would take to these modern, high-speed units, but they did. Many were amazed by the sheer power and smoothness, and both tractors (especially the 4010) were big hits.

The two new tractors were only slightly heavier than the equivalent old twins, but much more powerful. John Deere engineers could also point out that piston speeds were lower than in the twin, so the new engines shouldn't

Below: The 3010/4010 proved more successful than the smaller four-cylinder machines, which owed something to the old generation.

Above: John Deere's New Generation tractors were a big hit—nearly 60,000 4010s left the Waterloo production line.

Right: Engines, transmissions, and hydraulics—in almost every way, the big John Deeres leaped ahead of the opposition.

(in theory) wear out any faster, despite revving up to 2,500rpm.

Only one major problem afflicted the new engines. The blocks were sand cast, and sand left over from the production process would circulate in the coolant until it damaged the water pump O-rings, eventually causing leakage. So even these New Generation giants weren't entire trouble-free, but as far as John Deere was concerned, they could have been much worse. They were popular too. The company sold almost 45,000 3010s up to mid-1963, and not far short of 60,000 4010s. Everyone at Waterloo could breathe a sigh of relief.

5010

When it was launched, the 4010 was one of the most powerful tractors you could buy. But the tractor power race was in full swing now—the standard for big row-crop or wheatland tractors in America had risen from 50hp after World War II, to 60hp, then 70hp. In 1961, Allis-Chalmers launched the first mass produced turbocharged tractor, and every major manufacturer was planning something bigger. John Deere had no choice but to keep up.

So just two years after the launch of the New Generation, came the 5010, the first two-wheel-drive tractor with over 100hp at both PTO and drawbar. It was really a bigger version of the 4010, with all the same new features made familiar by

that 1960 launch. But unlike Allis-Chalmers, John Deere did not opt for turbocharging, instead offering a large (531ci/8.7 liter) six-cylinder diesel. There was no gasoline or LPG option, as diesel was now the power unit of choice among big tractors—the 4010 diesel would outsell its gas/LPG counterparts by ten to one.

Nebraska tested the new John Deere in October 1962, and recorded just over 121hp at the PTO at the rated 2,200rpm. On drawbar work, the 5010 could manage almost 106hp and a pull of 7,759lb. That sounded impressive, but it's worth noting that the Allis-Chalmers D21, announced the following year, was almost as powerful with a much smaller 421ci (6.9 liter) engine.

To cope with the power, a new tire size was developed (24.5-32 on the rears) and a twin rear wheel package—both were available as options

Above: With a tested drawbar pull of 7,700lb the 5010 had plenty of capacity. Those big tires were developed specifically to cope with the power.

for the standard model. With either of these, the 5010 could work in conditions that otherwise would have needed a crawler. But unlike a crawler, the big John Deere combined its great traction with relatively high road speeds.

Like its smaller brothers, the latest New Generation used the eight-speed Syncro-Range transmission, giving speeds of 1.75mph to 15.5mph. Plus of course, there was the impressive new hydraulic system, though the Nebraska testers found that the pump discs were failing after one of the PTO power tests—these had to be replaced before testing could continue.

Power brakes, power steering, and all the other new features that had so impressed the Dallas crowds in 1960, were there, and the 5010 could also be ordered with a factory-fitted cab, though this wasn't made by John Deere—that would come later, and it would set another new industry standard.

Left: The 100hp 5010 was very similar to the New Generation 4010, but with a larger 531ci (8.7 liter) engine.

8020

Remember the 8010, John Deere's pioneering super-tractor? With four-wheel-drive, full articulation, and over 200hp? All of these were common features on big tractors 20 years later, but in 1959 the 8010 was arguably ahead of its time. This was the machine JD launched as a prelude to the New Generation. It looked impressive on paper, and even more so in the field, especially given the ease with which it could pull an eight-bottom plough.

The onlookers were duly impressed but they didn't flock to buy it. Maybe it was too expensive, or too big, or too complex. Whatever the reason, it was not selling and the sales figures for 1960 stood at a dismal grand total of one.

Of those that did sell, most went to Mid-West wheat farmers—only two 8010s were actually sold east of the Mississippi. John Deere had to offer rental or leasing deals to persuade farmers to take the big tractor on at all.

Even once they had got the tractor out of the door, the problems weren't over. Many customers were disillusioned and sent them back to the factory, where some ended their days acting as giant yard tractors.

Confining one of these monster machines to yard duties seems a bit like chaining down King Kong.

As if that weren't enough, even the 8010s which stayed on farms caused further trouble. The nine-speed truck transmission wasn't up to the job, and every 8010 was eventually recalled and rebuilt with a heavier duty eight-speed transmission and clutch. They were also rebadged as 8020s, in order to reflect the amount of reworking that was involved. The power unit remained the GM 671E two-stroke diesel though, delivering a claimed 215hp at the PTO and 150hp at the drawbar.

It was 1965, nearly seven years after the original launch, before John Deere finally accepted that its first super-tractor was not a success, and ceased production—the exact figure is uncertain, but it's thought that around 100 left the factory.

But don't think this put John Deere off the concept altogether. In 1968/9 it offered the Wagner WA-14 and WA-17 in John Deere colors, as a holding operation until its own home grown successor to the 8010 was ready to roll out of the factory.

Above: The 8020 was a recalled rethink on the troublesome 8010, replacing the original truck transmission with a stronger eight-speed unit.

Left: With hindsight, the 8010 and 8020 were ahead of their time. Ten years later many farmers were happily spending big money on giant super-tractors, but not in the early 1960s.

3020/4020

John Deere 3020 (1963)

Engine type Four-cylinder ohv, water-cooled

Fuel type Gasoline

Bore x stroke 4.25 x 4.00in

Capacity 227ci (3.7 liters)

Rated speed 2,500rpm

TRANSMISSION

Transmission type Power Shift

Speeds 8F

Speed range 1.5-16.4mph

DIMENSIONS

Factory weight 7,695lb

Tested weight 9,495lb

Wheelbase 90in

Tire size F 6.00 x 16

Tire size R 15.5 x 38

Fuel tank (US gallons, main/aux) n/a

Cooling capacity (US gallons) n/a

PERFORMANCE

Power (at PTO) 64.1hp

Power (at drawbar) 54.6hp

Drawbar pull 4,006lb

Fuel efficiency 10.37hp/hr per gallon

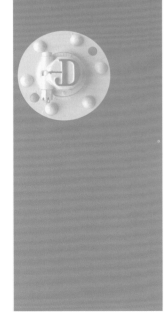

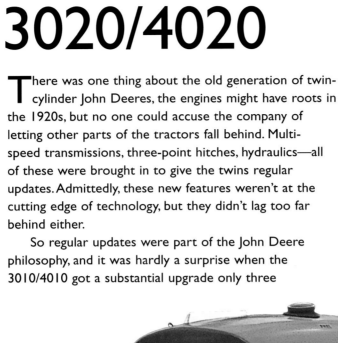

There was one thing about the old generation of twin-cylinder John Deeres, the engines might have roots in the 1920s, but no one could accuse the company of letting other parts of the tractors fall behind. Multi-speed transmissions, three-point hitches, hydraulics—all of these were brought in to give the twins regular updates. Admittedly, these new features weren't at the cutting edge of technology, but they didn't lag too far behind either.

So regular updates were part of the John Deere philosophy, and it was hardly a surprise when the 3010/4010 got a substantial upgrade only three

Above: This is the high clearance 3020 with ROPS and sun shield. Power was now up to 65hp at the PTO.

Above: The 4020, as pictured here, was John Deere's most popular model in the mid-1960s.

years after the New Generation had leapfrogged over the heads of a surprized competition. But that was the nature of the industry—to keep ahead, no tractor maker could afford to stand still. Indeed, John Deere himself had once admitted as much (though he wasn't talking about tractors): "We must continue to improve our product," he said, "or others will, and we will lose our trade." He had a good point.

Therefore the 3020/4020 were the first of the New Generation to be updated, and JD introduced a new Power Shift transmission that allowed clutchless on-the-go shifting between eight forward speeds and four reverse. It was a huge step forward, another advance on the two- or three-speed on-the-go range shifting that had first appeared in the mid 1950s. There was extra power too—the 3020 now offered 65hp at the PTO and the 4020 91hp. As before, there were several variations on the theme, and the 3020 came as Row-Crop, Row-Crop Utility, Standard, Hi-Crop, and Orchard models.

Even with these updates in production, the tractors were still given regular new features through the 1960s. The year after the 20-series appeared, they gained a

hydraulic differential lock. Controlled by a foot pedal, this ensured that power was supplied equally to both of the rear wheels, helping to reduce wheelspin on one. Or there was the option of hydrostatic front-wheel-drive from 1968. By then, John Deere was already offering the ROPS option—Roll Over Protection Structure—a strong roll cage that would protect the driver in the event of the tractor turning over. Every year, drivers were killed in roll-over accidents, and yet the ROPS was still not mandatory. John Deere famously offered all its research findings to the rest of the industry, in order to speed up the adoption of this vital safety feature.

Updates like this continued to build on the strong New Generation base, and made the 3020/4020 highly popular. The bigger tractor in particular was a real hit—over 27,000 were sold in the US and Canada in 1966 alone. That year, it accounted for almost half of John Deere's entire tractor sales.

110-140

It's often forgotten in the world of big, tough farm tractors, but John Deere has long been dominant in the lawn and garden tractor market as well. The first model appeared in 1963, the 7hp 110 powered by a Kohler single-cylinder engine. It marked the company's debut into the pure consumer market. It was later uprated to 8hp, and joined by the 10hp 112, all of which were styled to resemble the New Generation.

"See the NEW John Deere 110 Lawn and Garden Tractor," demanded the advert, "Try its exclusive Independent ground-speed control. Outstanding Features: 7hp 4-cycle engine. Ignition key (neutral gear) safety starter. Fiber glass hood and fenders. Brakes both rear wheels. Turns outside a 28-inch-radius circle." On top of all these attractive details it even had an adjustable rear wheel tread (27 or 33 inches) and boasted three forward speeds in seven speed ranges.

The 110 would be the first in a long line of Deere mini-tractors, being followed by the smaller 60 in 1966 and later the 70 and 100. All these were suitable for snow clearance as well as cutting grass.

A new range was introduced in 1978, and the 111 (now with 11hp) then remained best selling mini-tractor in the US right up to 1986. In the meantime, buyers were given a choice of five-speed transmission or automatic hydrostatic drive.

In the 1980s, John Deere's millionth mini-tractor rolled off the assembly line in Horicon, Wisconsin, and the machines themselves gradually acquired more sophistication. The 400 for example, brought power steering and the 332 and 430 had liquid-cooled diesel engines. They had become true mini-tractors rather than glorified sit-on lawn mowers, and most of the buyers were commercial rather than private.

Above: The 110 was first in a long line of John Deere mini-tractors, and had a simple specification.

Above: The 110 at work. Most of these early mini-tractors were used as ride-on lawn mowers, and bought by private owners as well as corporations.

Below: There were mini-accessories to suit the mini John Deeres, such as this neat little trailer.

5020

Year on year, the tractor power war progressed, and no manufacturer could afford to leave their flagship machines without a power increase every two or three years. In the early '60s, 100hp had been the target, and both John Deere (with the 5010) and Allis-Chalmers (with the D21) had obliged. Now it was 130hp or more, and once again John Deere was there. Just as the 5010 had been the first two-wheel-drive row crop with over 100hp at the drawbar (and the most powerful row-crop tractor on the market) so the 5020 did the same trick three years later.

It might seem odd to an outsider, that hard-nosed farmers, who had the same bottom line as any business manager, would be willing to spend more and more money on more and more powerful tractors. After all, the modern tractor was a business tool, not an emotional purchase. (Actually, in some cases it was probably a bit of both). But the bottom line was, and is, that bigger tractors can do more work, faster, than smaller ones—in the long-term, they actually pay for themselves and also save the farmer money.

But this is something of a double-edged sword. Encouraging farmers to work on an ever-larger scale means big profits for corporations like John Deere, and other agricultural players, such as the fertilizer manufacturers. Which is why these same corporations lobby government to support big farmers, often at the expense of small ones. But big farming provides fewer jobs and can be environmentally destructive into the bargain. So however technically interesting we find the big

Above: With 114hp at the drawbar, and 133hp at the PTO, this was the most powerful row-crop tractor customers could buy in 1966.

Above: Big wheeled, big horsepower 5020 could pull big implements, and save the farmer money in the long-term.

tractors, let's not forget that their effect on the environment isn't always benign.

Whatever its effect on the wider world, there's no argument that the John Deere 5020 was the most powerful tractor you could buy in 1966. Tested at Nebraska that September, it produced 133hp at the PTO and nearly 114hp at the drawbar.

What it didn't have was the latest Power Shift transmission (already offered on the 4020) which probably couldn't cope with 133hp. One point that did arise from the Nebraska test was that the 5020 wasn't as fuel-efficient as the old twin-cylinder Deere diesels, with a best figure of 16.89hp/hr per gallon. That was still pretty good, but then, it did have a lot to live up to.

JOHN DEERE V. ALLIS-CHALMERS

Model	5020	D21
Engine	531ci	426ci
Drawbar Power	114hp	110hp (est)
PTO Power	133hp	128hp
Weight	16,075lb	10,675lb

4520

SPECIFICATIONS

John Deere 4520 (1969)

Engine type Six-cylinder ohv turbo, water-cooled

Fuel type Diesel

Bore x stroke 4.25 x 4.75in

Capacity 404ci (6.6 liters)

Rated speed 2,200rpm

TRANSMISSION

Transmission type Power Shift

Speeds 8F

Speed range 1.7-18.5mph

DIMENSIONS

Factory weight 14,175lb

Tested weight 17,955lb

Wheelbase 106in

Tire size F 10.00 x 16

Tire size R 20.8 x 38

Fuel tank (US gallons, main/aux) n/a

Cooling capacity (US gallons) n/a

PERFORMANCE

Power (at PTO) 122.4hp

Power (at drawbar) 107.8hp

Drawbar pull 8,427lb

Fuel efficiency 15.08hp/hr per gallon

Allis-Chalmers' early use of a turbocharger to boost the power of its D19 diesel in 1961 did not lead to an immediate flurry of turbo-diesel activity amongst rival tractor makers. At first, the mainstream manufacturers relied on sheer cubic inches to power their ultimate row-crop machines. Giant super-tractors were different of course, and invariably used turbos to produce the massive horsepower they needed.

But one by one, tractor makers began to go the turbo route for their two-wheel-drive row-crop tractors as well. International followed Allis in 1965 with its 112hp Farmall 1206. Massey Ferguson followed up the year after, unveiling the 1130 (121hp). It was Oliver's turn in '67, offering the 106hp 1950-T. In 1969 Ford entered the fray, bringing the 131hp 9000 to market. And finally, that same year, John Deere joined in with the 4520, its first ever turbocharged row-crop, powered by the first turbo-diesel engine made in-house—previous John Deere turbos (the gargantuan 8010/8020) used a GM two-stroke diesel. The new engine was based on the existing 404ci (6.6 liter) six-cylinder unit already familiar in the 4020, though the lubrication system had to be doubled in capacity in order to cope with the higher stresses imposed by the turbo. The result was just over 122 PTO hp at the rated 2,200rpm and almost 108hp at the drawbar. It's interesting to compare these boosted figures to those of the 5010—they're almost identical, the older tractor achieving through sheer cubic capacity (531ci/8.7 liters) what the 4520 did with a turbo.

Not wishing to embarrass their biggest row-crop, Deere updated the 5010 which was rebadged as the 5020, with a modest power boost to keep it ahead of the turbo upstart. Transmission-wise, the 4520 came with a choice of eight-speed Syncro-Range or eight-speed Power Shift (still not available on the 5020). Both of these were tested at Nebraska, which found that the Syncro-Range proved slightly more fuel efficient, though of course the Power Shift saved time and was easier to operate. Speed ranges were very similar though: 1.95-18.3mph for the Syncro-Range, 1.7-18.5mph Power Shift.

Above: The 4520's turbo-diesel six had originated in this tractor (in non-turbo form), the 4020.

Right: Both 4020 (shown here) and the 4520 were of the pre-factory cab era, but that was about to change, with John Deere leading the way.

Left: John Deere finally took the turbo route in 1968 with the 4520. At 122 PTO hp, it was competitive machine but it did not lead the class.

4320/4620

SPECIFICATIONS

John Deere 4000 (1969)

Engine type Six-cylinder ohv, water-cooled

Fuel type Diesel

Bore x stroke 4.25 x 4.75in

Capacity 404ci (6.6 liters)

Rated speed 2,200rpm

TRANSMISSION

Transmission type Syncro Range

Speeds 8F

Speed range 1.8–16.8mph

DIMENSIONS

Factory weight 8,605lb

Tested weight 10,870lb

Wheelbase 96in

Tire size F 9.5 L x 15

Tire size R 16.9 x 34

Fuel tank (US gallons, main/aux) n/a

Cooling capacity (US gallons) n/a

PERFORMANCE

Power (at PTO) 96.9hp

Power (at drawbar) 82.6hp

Drawbar pull 5,464lb

Fuel efficiency 15.65hp/hr per gallon

Above: John Deere expanded its range of high-horsepower two-wheel-drive tractors in the early 1970s, to enable them to cover every possible gap in the market.

As the '60s turned into the '70s, John Deere was offering three high-horsepower two-wheel-drive tractors: 4020 (95hp), 4520 Turbo (122hp), and 5020 (133hp). A few years ago, that might have been acceptable, but now tractor models were multiplying as manufacturers sought to cover every conceivable gap in the market. There might well be farmers for whom a standard 4020 was not enough and a full-blown 4520 too much, which meant there was a gap in their range.

John Deere had two answers. The 4000 was one of them, partly a mix 'n match of existing components. It combined the 4020's engine with a lighter weight chassis similar to that of the superseded 4010. It therefore weighed in at 7,670lb, a whole 10% less than the 4040. The idea was to increase the power to weight ratio, so although the 4000 would use smaller implements than the 4020, it could pull them faster. It had a Syncro-Range transmission and Roll-Gard ROPS, though Power Shift and a canopy were both options.

The company's second solution to the 4020-4520 power gap was the 4320. This went in the opposite direction, adding 700lb to the 4020's weight, and with a lightly turbocharged version of the 404ci (6.6 liter) six—it produced 115hp, neatly bisecting the 4020 and 4520 gap. Again, this was quite close in specification to the 4020, with most of the same options and standard equipment, though it did have new 20.8 x 34 tires, to make the most of that 20% boost in power.

So far so good, but mean while the 5020 was starting to look outdated. It was big and heavy, with no Power Shift option, but again Deere was ready and waiting with an answer. This time it added an intercooler to the 4520 to create the 4620. Intercoolers are an effective means of improving the efficiency of turbo installations—by cooling the incoming air and therefore making it denser.

More air being forced into the cylinders, with more fuel to suit… equals more power, and the 4620 obliged with 136hp at the PTO, plus 116hp at the drawbar. In

Above: This shows an early cab on a 4320, but John Deere was about to make another great leap with the Generation II cab.

other words, much the same power as the 5020, but at 14,800lb, it weighed 2,550lb less. This new two-wheel-drive flagship came with eight-speed Syncro-Range or Power Shift, but it was only available for two years, as John Deere's Generation II was about to be unveiled.

MODEL RANGE

Model	Production Dates
4000	1968-72
4520 Turbo	1968-72
4320	1972-75
4620 Turbo	1972-75

Above: These most powerful tractors were still two-wheel-drive, but problems applying over 100hp to the ground forced a solution.

820-3120

If there had been one disappointing aspect to the John Deere New Generation, it was the smaller tractors, the 1010 and 2010. They lacked many of the features that made the bigger machines genuine steps forward, and the 1010 in particular suffered from engine problems.

This was all solved in 1965, when the 1020/2020 arrived. With many of those innovative New Generation features, these were perhaps the tractors that the 1010/2010 should have been in the first place. Even more significant, they were the company's first worldwide tractors—that is, designed to be built across the world in different factories, selling as many different models in different markets, but sharing many parts.

Ford was already making tractors in this way, with its Unified range, so JD was merely following the trend. John Deere's incentive was that it already owned the Lanz plant in Mannheim, Germany. Up until now, Mannheim-built Deeres had been quite different to the US machines, but the new worldwide tractor project offered the promise of sharply reduced costs through the use of shared parts.

So updating to the 1020/2020 held many

challenges. The specifications had to be acceptable on both sides of the Atlantic; manufacturing costs had to be 25% lower than before; and of course, the new 20 series had to be an improvement on the10. John Deere's designers succeeded in no uncertain terms: the 20 series could be built on the same tooling in both Mannheim and Dubuque; the 1020/2020 shared so many parts that 35% fewer compoents were needed to build them; they were cheaper to make too, so more profitable. That in turn allowed the designers to incorporate more features: eight-speed transmission, three-point hitch with lower link sensing, closed-centre hydraulics (a first on a utility tractor) and a live PTO. Roll-Gard ROPS was an option and the fuel tank was moved to the front, as on the bigger tractors.

A three-cylinder gasoline or diesel engine replaced the 1010's troublesome four, and the range of small 20 series was extended in both directions. In 1967, the three-cylinder 820, 920, and 1120 were introduced and the following year came the 2120, a turbocharged version of the 2020, with 72hp. For 1969, John Deere unveiled the six-cylinder 3120, with 86hp from its 303ci (5.0 liter) diesel.

Above: Not to be confused with... The small three-cylinder 820 shared its designation (but nothing else) with the king-size 820 twin of a decade earlier.

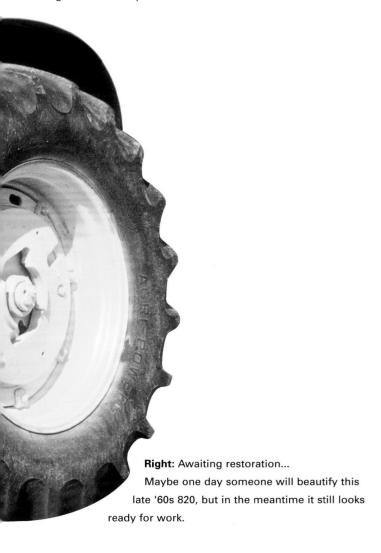

Above: The 820-3120 was John Deere's first worldwide tractor, designed to be acceptable on both sides of the Atlantic.

Right: Awaiting restoration...
Maybe one day someone will beautify this late '60s 820, but in the meantime it still looks ready for work.

7020/7520

Remember the 8010, John Deere's giant super-tractor that impressed farmers back in 1959, but not sufficiently to buy one? This was partly down to price—the 8010 cost $30,000, a massive sum at the time. It cost three times the price of a 5010 and few farmers could justify one. Ex-John Deere engineer Harold Brock later maintained that the 8010 was built mostly for testing.

But the company was still determined to produce a large four-wheel-drive tractor at reasonable cost, and work continued. In the meantime, it sold Wagner super-tractors in John Deere colours, the WA-14 and WA-17 of 1968-69.

Finally, in 1971, the company was ready for another go, unveiling the 7020. With full-time four-wheel-drive, an articulated chassis and high-mounted cab, this was built along the same format as other super-tractors (or for that matter, the original 8010 and the Wagner-built tractors). It was powered by a turbo-intercooled version of the company's 404ci (6.6 liter) six-cylinder diesel, enough for 146hp at the PTO.

So far so good, but what really made the big four-wheel-drive Deere work this time was its price. Quoted in "John Deere New Generation Tractors" (Chester Peterson Jr & Rod Beemer), Harold Brock later recalled how they did it. "What we did with the 7020," he said, "was to take the 4020 and bisect it and put an engine in the middle. By doing so we took advantage of high-volume

production components…and found that we could sell our tractor for $13,000. That put us in the four-wheel-drive business." Brock also pointed out that using existing parts made the new machine more readily serviceable by any local John Deere dealer.

Unlike other big four-wheel-drives, the 7020 was narrow enough to work row-crops, thanks to good visibility and adjustable wheel treads. What it didn't have was the massive power of some rivals. JD partially solved that in 1972 with the 7520, sporting a turbo-intercooler version of the ex-5010 531ci (8.7 liters) six-cylinder diesel—175hp at the PTO was better, but still not up to Steiger standards.

Left: By utilizing many existing components, John Deere was able to produce the four-wheel-drive 7020/7520 for a reasonable price.

Above: The 7020 with single wheels. Wide splined axles were designed to accept twin wheels relatively early.

Below: There is a big front loader on this 7520, the up-engined, uprated 7020.

830-6030

The early '70s were busy times for John Deere. Twelve years after the original New Generation launch at Dallas, the entire range was renewed or updated with the 30 series—Generation II.

Actually, the first Generation II tractors to appear were really just updates, rather than completely new models. The 2020 became 2030, with a 10% PTO power increase to 60hp for both gasoline and diesel versions. This would be the last gas John Deere tested at Nebraska, as sales had dwindled—on the bigger 4020, gasoline and LPG power made up just 1% of production each. Transmission was now constant-mesh with Hi-Lo or direction-reverser options.

The smaller 20 series were upgraded in 1973, as the Mannheim-built 830 (not to be confused with the big twin-cylinder diesel from Waterloo, built 15 years earlier) and 1530, while the Dubuque works added a 70hp 2630 to the 2030. (The older 820-1120 tractors were also available until 1975).

All four retained the old 20 series styling, rather than adopt the new look of the bigger Generation II tractors. The idea was to save money (it wasn't cheap to built small tractors in the US or Germany, compared to Italy or Japan) so this was emphasized in the publicity.

"John Deere announces 4 new low-priced tractors. New models. New power

sizes. And far more honest value for the money you invest. That's our promise and that's the story on these four new John Deere Diesel Tractors in the 35- to 70-horsepower class. These four new tractors have list prices that range from several hundred to nearly a thousand dollars below the suggested list prices of two major competitors… you'll change your thinking about John Deere Tractor prices… More buying power to you."

A very different machine was the big 6030, though this too was updated rather than all-new. The 6030 adopted the mantle of the original 5010, acting as John Deere's top-power two-wheel-drive tractor. Announced in March 1972, it came with a choice of six-cylinder diesels, both of them turbo-intercooled: the 146hp 404ci (6.6 liter) diesel from the 4620, or the 7520's 175hp unit (531ci/8.7 liters).

Above: Flashback: Not a 1970s 830, but a very different tractor from the late '50s, albeit with the same number. John Deere restorers and historians beware!

Left: Two six-cylinder turbo-intercooled diesels were available on the big 6030: 146hp 404ci (6.6 liters) or 175hp 531ci (8.7 liters).

4030-4630

SPECIFICATIONS

John Deere 4630 (1972)

Engine Type Six-cylinder turbo-intercooled, water-cooled

Fuel type Diesel

Bore x stroke 4.25 x 4.75in

Capacity 404ci (6.6 liters)

Rated speed 2,200rpm

TRANSMISSION

Transmission type Power Shift

Speed 8F

Speed range 1.7-17.7mph

DIMENSIONS

Factory weight 16,250lb

Tested weight n/a

Wheelbase 112in

Tire size F 10.00 x 16

Tire size R 18.4 x 38

Fuel tank (US gallons, main/aux) n/a

Cooling capacity (US gallons) n/a

PERFORMANCE

Power (at PTO) 150.7hp

Power (at drawbar) 127.9hp

Drawbar pull 10,571lb

Fuel efficiency 15.68hp/hr per gallon

Hitch lift 5,260lb

Some people say that the Generation II John Deeres, launched in August 1972, had as great an impact as the original Dallas generation of 1960. Whether they did or not, they certainly marked a huge step forward in tractor design, in fact, there were several.

Most obvious was the Sound Gard cab. John Deere had led the US tractor industry in developing and offering effective roll-over protection systems. Now it did the same with an all-new cab that set new standards for quietness and comfort. Until then, many cabs, even if factory-fitted, were proprietory units, bolted on as afterthoughts rather than designed into the tractor. In hot weather, they could be dusty, noisy, and unpleasant.

The Sound Gard cab was very different. It was spacious and glassy, with tinted glass to help keep the sun's rays at bay. Quieter than any other cab on the market (so quiet, that you could pay extra for a radio cassette) it had the option of a pressurizer to keep dust and dirt out, and a heater or air conditioning.

Now these features are taken for granted on modern tractors, but in 1972 this was ground breaking stuff. There were seat belts, a tilt-telescope steering wheel and underslung pedals. Most significant of all, four-post ROPS was standard. The Sound Gard option wasn't cheap, but over half of John Deere 30 series buyers opted to pay for it. Within a year, it changed the perception of tractor cabs from an occasional option to virtual necessity.

There were other new features on the 30 series, notably the Perma-Clutch, which was oil cooled and extended the clutch life. The faithful Syncro-Range

Below: The new cab offered far superior visibility compared to the earlier cabs, and as an added bonus it also provided unheard-of comfort and quietness for the driver.

Above: Just for comparison, here's an earlier cab, showing the smaller glass area, intrusive pillars, but generous space.

transmission was still standard, but a new Quad Range, with 16 speeds was offered by adding a Hi-Lo power shift to the Syncro-Range. The bigger 30 series also had a full Power Shift option.

Four tractors made up the new range, all powered by six-cylinder diesels: the 80hp 4030 replaced the four-cylinder 3020; the 100hp 4230 was an update of the 4020, powered by the familiar six-cylinder 404ci (6.6 liter) unit. Best seller in the new range was the turbocharged 4430, with 125hp, while an intercooled 4630 (150hp) topped off the range.

Above: The Sound Gard cab, with its huge glass area and wrap around windscreen, is clearly visible in this shot.

MODEL RANGE

Model	Production Dates
4030	1968-72
4230	1968-72
4430 Turbo	1972-75
4630 Turbo-intercooled	1972-75

8430/8630

The last tractors to acquire 30 series designation were the big four-wheel-drives—in late 1974 the 7020 and 7520 became 8430 and 8630 respectively. Most significant of all, they received a power boost. This was essential—not only where super-tractor rivals offering more and more horsepower, but the two-wheel-drives were starting to catch up, with over 150hp on the top models.

For the renumbered John Deere 8000s (a revival of the original 8000 tag) the extra power came from bigger engines. The 7020's engine was bored out to 466ci (7.6 liters), with power up by 20% to 178hp at the PTO—that made up the new 8430.

The 8630 had an extra half-inch on the bore (the five-inch stroke was unchanged), which translated into 619ci (10.0 liters) and 225 PTO hp. It was the first John Deere built in-house to finally top the power of the original 8010.

Both super-tractors retained the ability to work row-crops, while the three-point hitch was updated to a 3-N type, able to use both Category 2 and Category 3 implements. They also shared the new, chunkier styling of the Generation II tractors, and the glassy Sound Gard cab. Both had 16-speed transmission with partial-range power shifting—that is, two ranges of eight speeds, with power shift between them.

Nebraska tested the 8630 in June 1975, and found it tipped the scales at 26,480lb including front wheel ballast and using the standard 23.1-30 inch tires. The speed ranged from 2.0mph in low range to just over 20mph in high, and the usual two-hour economy run (in sixth gear) produced 13.67hp/hr per gallon. On the same test, the big John Deere also managed just short of 200hp at

the drawbar—198.12, to be exact. Rated at 2,100rpm, John Deere's own big six-cylinder diesel churned out 225.59hp at the PTO, and with no driveline losses involved, 15.34hp/hr per gallon.

Now with competitive power, these big four-wheel-drive super-tractors still sold in relatively small numbers, as only the larger farms could justify their extra cost. In 1975 for example, John Deere sold nearly 14,000 4430s (its best selling tractor that year) but less than 2,000 8630s and 1,336 8430s. Together, the super-tractors made up just 6% of John Deere sales in the US and Canada.

Left: More power (now up to 225hp at the PTO) and the Sound Gard cab marked the first major update of John Deere's biggest tractor.

Above: There are twin wheels fitted to this 8630— the triple wheels, that came much later, became an option on the big John Deeres. Rubber tracks came later still.

Below: The classic super-tractor profile, all engine and cab on an articulated chassis.

2040-2940

No sooner had the biggest John Deeres gained the 30 series tag, than they were "overtaken" by an updated 40 series of utility tractors. After three years as the 830-2630, Deere's smallest tractors (lawn-bound tiddlers excepted) were updated with more powerful engines and new styling. The latter of these was now closer to that of the large Generation II row-crops, with the same blunt front end.

As before, production was a joint effort between Mannheim and Dubuque. The three-cylinder 2040 (40hp) and 2240 (50hp) came from Germany, both with 5hp more than the 2030 and 2230 respectively. The American factories, however, still supplied the four-cylinder utilities, now the 60hp 2440 and 70hp 2640. To round off the list of new products, a six-cylinder utility—the 80hp 2840— was added early the following year, and that one was Mannheim-built.

Although these machines were all utility tractors, competing at the cheaper end of the market, they could be equipped to much higher standards, with many "big tractor" features. Power steering, hydraulic brakes, and a live PTO were all on the options list, as was an adjustable swinging drawbar and differential lock, the latter engageable without stopping.

For Europe, the 30 series of 830, 930, 1030, 1130, 1630, 2030, and 2230 continued, but with Generation II styling, and the option of a safety cab. Another new option was hydraulic front-wheel-assist for the 2130/3130 and a mechanical four-wheel-drive system for the smaller tractors the following year. The top 3130 now offered 97hp from is 329ci (5.4 liter) six-cylinder diesel.

For 1979, the full Sound Gard cab was finally offered on John Deere's smaller tractors. At the same time, the 830-

Above: John Deere's smaller tractors were made at the American factory at Dubuque, or at Mannheim in Germany.

3130 became the 840-3140, which ran through to 1986. There were several variations on the theme, such as the 1981 S series with extra power—some examples of these were the 75hp 2040S and 4240S.

Reflecting the hard times, an economy range—the X-E models—was unveiled three years later and was available on the 1640, 2040, 2040S, and 2140. Meanwhile, the 2840 had become 2940 (with larger 359ci/5.9 liter engine) and all the small 40 series received new styling, with an up-sloping hood that was required for the fitment of the Sound Gard cab.

And so to summarize in the words of the John Deere marketing material: "You can almost call it 'genetic engineering.' Adding a new John Deere option like Sound-Gard body to the 2940 and spreading new features across the 40- to 80-hp tractor line-up spurs productivity on every job you do."

Left: Whether named a 30 or 40 series, these smaller and mid-sized tractors maintained John Deere's presence within the sub-80hp market.

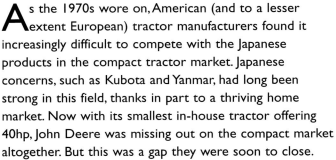

650-1650

SPECIFICATIONS

John Deere 1250 (1982)

Engine type: Three-cylinder, water-cooled

Fuel type Diesel

Bore x stroke 3.74 x 4.33in

Capacity 143ci (2.3 liters)

Rated speed 2,500rpm

TRANSMISSION

Transmission type Sliding gear

Speeds 9F

Speed range 1.2-15.4mph

DIMENSIONS

Factory weight 5,090lb

Tested weight 5,180lb

Wheelbase 75in

Tire size F 9.5 x 24

Tire size R 14.9 x 28

Fuel tank (US gallons, main/aux) n/a

Cooling capacity (US gallons) n/a

PERFORMANCE

Power (at PTO) 40.7hp

Power (at drawbar) 33.7hp

Drawbar pull 2,232lb

Fuel efficiency 16.69hp/hr per gallon

Hitch lift 2,240lb

Cab noise 94.5dB(A)

As the 1970s wore on, American (and to a lesser extent European) tractor manufacturers found it increasingly difficult to compete with the Japanese products in the compact tractor market. Japanese concerns, such as Kubota and Yanmar, had long been strong in this field, thanks in part to a thriving home market. Now with its smallest in-house tractor offering 40hp, John Deere was missing out on the compact market altogether. But this was a gap they were soon to close.

Designing its own compact range from scratch would have been expensive and time consuming—it made a lot more sense to buy-in tractors from Japan, and sell them in John Deere colors through its own dealers.

So that's what they did in late 1977—after a long period of talks, it was agreed that John Deere would sell Yanmar tractors in the US, badged and painted as John Deeres. Not that they were 100% Japanese imports though, for example the first two models to be offered—the 22hp 850 and 27hp 950—were both powered by John Deere's own three-cylinder diesel engine.

In the way of Japanese compact tractors, they were quite sophisticated, true miniaturized full-size machines rather than cut-price specials—deservedly, the advertising slogan described them as the "Little Big Tractors." As a result buyers got an eight-speed two-lever transmission giving 1-12mph. There was also a differential lock (which could be engaged on the move), a 540rpm PTO with overrun clutch, and Category 1 three-point hitch. You could even choose to have mechanical front-wheel-drive as an added extra.

A complete range of implements was available as well, underlining the point that the Yanmars were serious small tractors: ploughs, disks, toolbars, a rotary cutter, front loader, and backhoe. The most popular though, was the mowing attachment, reflecting the predominant buyer was the home owning, not the farmer.

After a couple of years, the range was extended upwards with the 33hp 1050 and in 1982 by the 40hp 1250. The company also decided to produce two smaller machines aimed purely at the consumer market—the 17hp 650 and 20hp 750. In fact, the Yanmar line was permitted to overlap the smallest Mannheim-built tractors, at least in power, with a four-cylinder 50hp 1450 and turbocharged 60hp 1650 which were introduced to the range in 1984.

The two line-ups continued to appeal to these two different markets, with the heavier more traditional Mannheim machines still favoured by farmers. John Deere did introduce a more farm-orientated Yanmar though, the 25hp 900HC in 1986, aimed at single-row cultivation for nursery and tobacco farmers.

Compact tractors, as well as the small lawn and garden machines, would remain part of the John Deere line-up for many years to come—the Yanmar imports had certainly done a good job.

Below Left: The biggest Yanmar machines grew out of the compact market, to overlap with John Deere's own Mannheim-built small tractors.

Above: : ROPS (Roll Over Protection System) was standard on this 750, as it was on all the Yanmar-derived compacts.

Below: The complete line-up—note the use of lawn tires on some models, and more aggressive treads for field use and/or with front-wheel-assist.

4040-4840

"New Iron Horses" was the marketing name for John Deere's latest big row-crop tractors in the late 1970s. Unlike the Yanmar-derived compact tractors, or even the smaller Mannheim-built models, these were designed and built in America, primarily for American farmers. They remained John Deere's best selling range, and could trace their ancestry back to the 4010 of 1960, in spirit, if not in components. They were also the last John Deere to offer a twin-front-wheel tricycle option. This had gradually become less popular, as the distinction between "row-crop" and "standard tread" tractors grew irrelevant. From the early '80s onwards, all John Deeres came with twin front wheels.

But the most significant thing about the Iron Horses weren't their size or the number of wheels they had, but their new six-cylinder diesel engine. Apart from the entry-level 4040, which continued with the venerable 90hp 404ci (6.6 liters) unit all the big 40-series made use of a new 466ci (7.6 liter) engine. This came in naturally aspirated 110hp form

(in the 4240), 130hp turbo (4440) and 155 turbo-intercooled (4640). There was also a new flagship, the 180hp 4840, powered by a hopped-up version of that same 466ci six-cylinder diesel. This effectively replaced the old 6030. But of the five Iron Horses, the relatively mild 4440 was to prove the best seller.

Along with the new engine came a substantially uprated cooling system, with bigger radiators, water pumps, and fans. (So that's why Deere was able to offer a two-year warranty on the new engine). The fuel injection pumps were new too, and all models

Above: The Sound Gard cab was familiar, but not the new 466ci (7.6 liter) six-cylinder diesel.

benefited from a beefier alternator. As for transmission, the big 4840 had an eight-speed Power Shift as standard, while the other four had to make do with a 16-speed Quad-Range, which allowed partial power shifting only. The full Power Shift was an option, and in fact most of the 40 series tested at Nebraska were equipped with this system.

Finally, the hydraulic capacity was increased substantially, to allow for remote cylinders and loaders, while all 40 series received a bigger fuel tank. The latter was introduced in response to farmers' requests—they wanted to be able to spend a long day in the field without refuellling. Now they could.

Above: There were twin front wheels for all-new John Deeres now, as the old distinction between row-crop and standard machines faded away.

Below: Once again the fine visibility of the Sound Gard cab is obvious here—every rival sought to catch up with its own new cab.

8440/8640

SPECIFICATIONS

John Deere 8640 (1979)

Engine type Six-cylinder turbo-intercooled, water-cooled

Fuel type Diesel

Bore x stroke 5.13 x 5.0in

Capacity 619ci (10.1 liters)

Rated speed 2,100rpm

TRANSMISSION

Transmission type Quad Range

Speeds 16F

Speed range 2.1-20.2mph

DIMENSIONS

Factory weight 28,270lb

Tested weight n/a

Wheelbase 125in

Tire size F 23.1 x 34 twins

Tire size R 23.1 x 34 twins

Fuel tank (US gallons, main/aux) n/a

Cooling capacity (US gallons) n/a

PERFORMANCE

Power (at PTO) 228.8hp

Power (at drawbar) 203.3hp

Drawbar pull 13,670lb

Fuel efficiency 15.61hp/hr per gallon

Hitch lift 8,545lb

Cab noise 80.0 dB(A)

Just as the Iron Horses were upgraded with a 40 series update, so were the four-wheel-drives, though not until 1979. The 8440 (replacing the 8430) and 8640 (8630) were marginally more powerful than the tractors they succeeded, by just a couple of horsepower apiece on the PTO figure. And yet they were astonishingly expensive. The 8440 leapt in price from just over $43,000 (four years earlier) to over $63,000, while for the 8640, John Deere was asking $77,628. Other John Deere tractors were affected in the same way at around this time, so it was indicative of a high inflation economy.

But behind the tiny power increases, and an exterior appearance that barely changed at all, there were many improvements under the skin. Both big four-wheel-drives now had a hitch lift of 8,545lb, an increase of over 30% for the 8440. Both had quieter cabs too, and despite the modest power boost, both had substantially more drawbar pull than the tractors they replaced—now 28,270lb for the 8640, up by nearly 1,800lb.

Front and rear hydraulic differential locks were now optional and the Quad-Range transmission control was simplified, with a single lever. There were now four remote cylinder outlets for the hydraulics. The driver got a HydraCushioned seat

Above: Quieter cabs, more hitch lift, and extra drawbar pull summed up the 40 series super-tractors.

(Deere's copy writers had clearly been hard at work) and and an Investigator warning system that monitored several engine and power train components.

These might have been the biggest, most powerful John Deeres ever, but by the power standards of the late 1970s super-tractors, the 8440 and 8640 were nothing special. Although International's "Super Snoopys"—the 3388 and 3588—were no threat at 130 and 150hp respectively, John Deere's arch rival also offered the 4786, V8, with 265hp.

Plenty of other manufacturers jostled for space in the 250hp-plus market. Massey-Ferguson's four-wheel-drive offered up to 273hp and the Allis Chalmers 8550 put out 254hp. Ford's FW-40 and 60 used massive Cummins V8s, with or without turbo, to give 240 or 282hp. Then there were the specialists: in 1979/80, buyers could choose from the Versatile 935 (282hp), Steiger Tiger III (372hp), and Big Bud 525/50 (525hp estimated), the latter powered by a 1,150ci (18.7 liter) Cummins six.

No doubt about it, if John Deere wanted to compete with these giants of the praries, it would have to come up with a bigger engine. And that was on the way...

Left: Want one? In 1979, it would cost you over $60,000 for the 8440, near $80,000 for the 8640. Inflation was taking its toll.

4050-4850

SPECIFICATIONS

John Deere 4450 (1983)

Engine type Six-cylinder turbo, water-cooled

Fuel type Diesel

Bore x stroke 4.56 x 4.75in

Capacity 466ci (7.6 liters)

Rated speed 2,200rpm

TRANSMISSION

Transmission type Quad Range

Speeds 16F

Speed range 2.0-17.3mph

DIMENSIONS

Factory weight 14,300lb

Tested weight 16,680lb

Wheelbase 107in

Tire size F 10.00 x 16

Tire size R 18.4 x 38

Fuel tank (US gallons, main/aux) n/a

Cooling capacity (US gallons) n/a

PERFORMANCE

Power (at PTO) 140.3hp

Power (at drawbar) 120.1hp

Drawbar pull 8,954lb

Fuel efficiency 16.36hp/hr per gallon

Hitch lift 6,294lb

Cab noise 73.5 dB(A)

The 1980s were very difficult times for US tractor manufacturers. A long-term agricultural slump and cheap imports combined to force down demand. This affected John Deere no less than any other concern, though they alone out of the American big names, were able to survive without merger or takeover. However, it did make half of its workforce redundant, which amounted to thousands of jobs lost, on top of the farm closures during the decade.

Still, the company was perhaps in a stronger position than most of its rivals. In 1979, the high point in US tractor sales before the slump set in, it was unchallenged leader of the North American market, with sales (of all farm equipment) not far short of $4 billion. Then the recession began to bite, and every manufacturer—no matter how old and well respected its name—was fighting for its life.

It was against this background of a depressed market that the 50 series was launched: an ambitious update of both Mannheim utility and Waterloo-built row-crop tractors at the same time. Launching ten new models (not to mention the

new V8-powered 8850) was expensive, but in doing so the company was merely following John Deere's original maxim, that you have to keep investing, or get sidelined by the competition.

So there were modest power increases right across the Waterloo range, which now comprized: 100hp 4050, 120hp 4250, 140hp 4450, 165hp 4650, and 190hp 4850. Perhaps bigger news was the new 15-speed Power Shift transmission, which was standard on the 4850 and optional on the rest—it was the next step forward in tractor transmissions, offering full power shift over a

Left: Beneath the skin, John Deere's big Waterloo-built tractors could be bought with a full power shift for the first time.

Above: The increasingly popular sport of tractor pulling benefited from ever bigger, more powerful engines.

multi-speed range. There was also the new Castor/Action mechanical front-wheel-drive, which unlike the earlier system allowed 13 degrees of castor (wheel lean) and a tight turning circle, thanks in part to pivoting the axle above the central front differential. As a result the greater turning clearance allowed the space for bigger front wheels, which benefited traction, and more customers opted for this system than for the previous hydrostatic arrangment.

Inside the cab, there was a development of the Investigator system first seen on the 40 series super-tractors, the electronic Investigator II. Cab noise was down too, to just 70.0dB(A) for a 4050 working at half load. In fact, the 50 series set a new record at Nebraska, for the quietest tractor ever tested. There were some changes to the hydraulics—selective control valves and breakaway couplers—and a Quik-Coupler hitch was standard on the 4650 and 4850.

Alongside the big 50 series were the smaller utilities, now all built at Mannheim. These ranged from the three-cylinder 45hp 2150 to the six-cylinder 85hp 2950. These too offered Castor/Action mechanical front-wheel-drive and there was a new eight-speed TSS (top-shaft-synchronized) transmission, with Hi-Lo or direction reverser options. A 95hp 3150 was added in 1985, with mechanical front-wheel-drive as standard, this engaging automatically when it was needed. There were also lots of special variations for orchard work, high-crop clearance and wide-row crops.

8450-8850

Remember how John Deere didn't have a sufficiently big and beefy diesel with which to contest the 250hp plus market? The early 1980s didn't seem like a propitious time to launch one, especially as the company had its corporate hands full renewing and updating the entire two-wheel-drive range at the time. But even in the tough 1980s, farmers were still buying super-tractors (albeit in smaller numbers than before) so John Deere took the decision to go ahead with its largest, most powerful tractor ever, the 8850.

Perhaps the most surprising thing about the 8850 wasn't that it arrived in the midst of a recession, but that it was powered by an engine that John Deere had designed by itself. Many of the biggest super-tractors used off-the-shelf power units—often from Cummins—but Deere decided to build its own V8. It used the same five-inch stroke as the big six-cylinder Deeres, but there the resemblance ended.

Combined with a bore of 5.51 inches, this produced a capacity of 955ci (15.6 liters), and it was both turbocharged and intercooled. Rated at 2,100rpm, it could provide 304hp at the PTO, with almost 270hp of drawbar pull, according to Nebraska, and a maximum of 35,330lb

of pull in second gear. The standard transmission was a 16-speed with partial range power shifting, giving 2.1 to just over 20mph. Whatever engine was used, there's no doubt that John Deere finally had its top-power contender.

Despite their huge power, the three four-wheel-drives were advertised as "Three new ways to tighten your belt," reflecting the hard times, though at $118,000 the 8850 was hardly an economy item. There were some moves to improve efficiency though, such as mixed-flow fans on the updated 8450 and 8650, and a viscous fan for the 8850, which was temperature sensitive and only ran when needed. Both six-cylinder 4x4s had slightly more power than before (8450—185hp, 8650—235hp).

Visibility was improved over the 40 series, by moving the air cleaner intake and the muffler to the right of the cab, while servicing was made easier by grouping all the check points together. There were new ISO remote hydraulic couplers and a Category 4/4N Quik-Coupler hitch on the 8850. Oh, and the 8850 buyer got six headlights on the front of his tractor, to ensure that everyone knew that, recession or not, he'd just laid out a six-figure sum on a tractor.

Below: Six headlamps denotes the V8 8850, powered by John Deere's biggest engine ever.

Above: Super-tractors were created for very large fields such as this one—few were sold in Europe.

Below: If the V8 was too much, John Deere still offered a choice of six-cylinder super-tractors, with 185hp or 235hp.

4055-4955

SPECIFICATIONS

John Deere 4955 (1989)

Engine type Six-cylinder turbo-intercooled, water-cooled

Fuel type Diesel

Bore x stroke 4.56 x 4.75in

Capacity 466ci (7.6 liters)

Rated speed 2,100rpm

TRANSMISSION

Transmission type
Power Shift

Speeds 15F

Speed range
1.4-19.3mph

DIMENSIONS

Factory weight
18,370lb

Tested weight n/a

Wheelbase 118in

Tire size F n/a

Tire size R n/a

PERFORMANCE

Power (at PTO) 202.7hp

Power (at drawbar) 170.7hp

Drawbar pull 23,742lb

Fuel efficiency (PTO)
18.39hp/hr per gallon

Fuel efficiency (drawbar)
14.63hp/hr per gallon

Hitch lift 9,710lb

Cab noise 76.5 dB(A)

Above: The 4955 was John Deere's first 200hp row-crop tractor.

If any old-timer Deere employees thought nothing would ever top the 1960 New Generation launch at Dallas, they would have been surpised by Palm Springs. Here in January 1989, the company made its biggest-ever launch presentation. It wasn't a huge range—just six updated machines, with lots of parts in common—but again the company was putting its money where its mouth was, investing in new models and lavish launches while US tractor sales continued to languish. The slump that had begun in 1980 was still ongoing, and it would be another four years before sales began the long climb back up.

The new 55 series followed directly on from the Waterloo-built 50 series, but the range was now divided in two, with either 106-inch wheelbase (4055, 4255, and 4455, the "narrow-frame" tractors) or 118-inch with a wider hood (4555, 4755, and 4955).

What they all shared was a totally redesigned 466ci (7.6 liter) six-cylinder diesel engine. There were new turbochargers of greater capacity than before, new 7-hole injector nozzles, new valves and ports, and higher top pistons rings. All the fans were viscous temperature-controlled.

The result was more power and efficiency—in that John Deere diesel tradition, the 55 series set a new record for fuel efficiency at Nebraska. In fact, even the Made-in-Japan Yanmar had set a new efficiency record when tested in John Deere colors—maybe it was something to do with the green-and-yellow livery! Whatever the reason, it didn't seem to harm power outputs: the base 4055 now offered 105hp, and there was a steady increase up through the new 155hp 4555 to the range-topping 200hp 4955, the latter being John Deere's first 200hp row-crop.

Transmission options were much as before, with the 16-speed Quad-Range and Perma-Clutch standard on all but the top tractor, which used the 15-speed Power Shift. That was optional on the others. Castor/Action MFWD featured as well, but now the automatic engagement/disengagement could be switched on or off. There was an electro-hydraulic hitch control on the three 116-inch wheelbase tractors, with a lift capacity of up to 10,000lb on the 4955.

But these weren't the first 55 series John Deeres. The Mannheim utility tractors had been updated as 55s two years earlier. As before, they offered many of

the same features as the big Waterloo machines, such as Castor/Action mechanical front-wheel-drive, 16-speed Hi-Lo transmission, hydraulic direction reverser, and also a 12-speed creeper set up. Many of these machines were sold for orchard or vineyard use, and two new high-clearance models—a 2755 and 2955—were launched between 1987 and 1988.

As for the standard range, that comprised of a 3-cylinder 45hp 2155 and 55hp turbo 2355N (both vineyard/orchard machines); 4-cylinder 55hp 2355 and turbo 65hp 2555; 75hp 2755, 80hp 2833N, and 85hp 2955. What with these, the Yanmar compacts, Waterloo 55s, and the super-tractor series, John Deere had just about every niche in the market covered as the 1990s began. This meant that in 1993, when overall tractor sales finally turned upwards, it was making profits again.

Below: Twin-wheel option fitted on this 4955, which was sometimes essential to get 200hp to the ground without excessive wheel slip.

8560-8960

SPECIFICATIONS

John Deere 8960 (1989)

Engine type Six-cylinder turbo-intercooled, water-cooled

Fuel type Diesel

Bore x stroke 5.50 x 6.00in

Capacity 855ci (13.9 liters)

Rated speed 1,900rpm

TRANSMISSION

Transmission type PowrSync

Speeds 24F

Speed range 2.2-23.2mph

DIMENSIONS

Factory weight 35,570lb

Tested weight n/a

Wheelbase 134in

Tire size F n/a

Tire size R n/a

PERFORMANCE

Power (at PTO) 333.4hp

Power (at drawbar) 308.3hp

Drawbar pull 34,316lb

Fuel efficiency (PTO) 17.08hp/hr per gallon

Fuel efficiency (drawbar) 14.26hp/hr per gallon

Hitch lift 13,940lb

Cab noise 74.0 dB(A)

Alongside the 55 series at John Deere's biggest ever launch at Palm Springs were the latest 60 series four-wheel-drives, though they had actually been unveiled months before in Denver the previous year. A quick glance suggested that they had hardly changed, but really this latest incarnation of the biggest John Deeres was almost completely new.

Built around a new, longer wheelbase chassis, they really went up a power class. The lowest powered John Deere super-tractor was now the 8560, with 200hp at the PTO, powered by the same 466ci (7.6 liter) diesel as the 4955. The overlap was intentional, to give buyers the choice between a four-wheel-drive articulated machine and a conventional two-wheel-drive, with the same power. Fortunate was the farmer who could choose between the two, without bothering too much about the $20,000 difference in price! The 8560, for the record, came in at $100,950.

Next up was the 8760, successor to the 8650. Like the 8560, this carried on with the same John Deere six-cylinder diesel as before, in this case the 619ci (10.1 liter) that had powered the mid-range four-wheel-drive Deere since the mid 1970s. But just as the 8560 got a modest power boost, so did this one, from 239hp at the PTO to 256hp—as ever, all figures are taken from the Nebraska tests. That translated into a drawbar pull of 32,880lb, a significant increase on its predecessor's which was around 28,000lb. It wasn't as efficient as the 200hp 60 series though, with 16.3hp/hr per gallon at maximum PTO power against 17.2.

And the top of the range 60 series? Well the surprise was that John Deere dropped its 955ci (15.6 liters) turbo-intercooled V8 in favor of a straight six from Cummins. The V8, which John Deere also offered for industrial

Below: For the 1990s, John Deere's super-tractor went up a power class, starting at 200 PTO hp, with up to 304hp from the Cummins-powered 8960.

Above: Just one indicator of what one driver and a super-tractor could do—work rates like this made economic sense of those six-figure price tags.

applications, made 304hp at the PTO, and 274hp at the drawbar. By comparison, the Cummins six was smaller, with a bore and stroke of 5.5 x 6.0 inches for a capacity of 855ci (13.9 liters), and ran at a lower rated speed (1,900rpm versus 2,100rpm). And yet it was over 10% more powerful, with 333hp at the PTO with 308hp at the drawbar, (though measured in pounds, the pull was actually slightly lower). The new tractor could cope with much heavier implements too, with a hitch lift of 13,940lb, up from just over 10,000. It was also quieter for the driver, with 74.0dB(A) in the cab instead of 78.0dB(A).

Engines aside, there was a choice of three new transmissions for all three 60 four-wheel-drives: 12-speed Synchro, 24-speed PowrSyn with built-in Hi-Lo, and a 12-speed Power Shift. Triple tires were another option available to the buyer, necessary in order to maximize traction. The 60s series also had a new side-access door and a one-piece upper windscreen. They are also easy to tell apart from their predecessors as they have a small sloping front grille above the headlamps.

455-955

By the mid-1980s, John Deere had a long and lucrative track record in the production of mini-tractors, whether for lawn and garden work, golf courses, or municipal duties. Some of the larger models were also used for light farm work, or by market gardeners, and the specification of these tractors had advanced to reflect these varied uses, and of course the growing expectations of the customer. John Deere's mini-tractors of the 1980s and '90s were a far cry from that first 110 of 1963, with its simple air-cooled single-cylinder engine of just 7hp.

Those early US-made mini-tractors were much later supplanted by rebadged Yanmar machines, painted in John Deere colors, and in the mid-1980s the company was still pursuing a dual-source strategy for its mini-tractors, offering both repainted Yanmars and those built at its plant in Horicon, Wisconsin.

In 1986, a new 55 series was introduced, with hydrostatic drive and aimed at the sub-40hp market. Initially the line-up consisted of the 655, 755, and 855, though a higher powered 955 was added three years later, offering 33hp at the flywheel. The smallest 655 was dropped in 1990, but three years on again, John Deere slipped in the 455 to plug the bottom of the range, this one with 22hp. Really, these machines deserved their modern term of "compact" tractors, rather than mini-tractors, being far more powerful and sophisticated than the small lawn tractors originally aimed at private buyers. In fact, the market had since changed in any case, with commercial and municipal customers now outranking the private buyer.

Meanwhile, the Yanmar line up was updated too. This had originally been introduced as a 50 series in 1978, spanning 650 to 1650, though all used John Deere's own engines rather than Yanamar units. In 1989, they were replaced with a 70 series, all of which were gear-driven (unlike Deere's own hydrostatic-drive 55 series). The new range kicked off with the 18.5hp 670, with a three-cylinder engine. The 28hp 870 was top of the three-cylinder range, while the 33hp 970 and range-topping 1070 (the latter with 38.5hp) had four-cylinder units.

These were sophisticated compacts indeed.

Specifications here are for JD's latest lawn tractor,

Left: The 455 model was John Deere's smallest compact tractor, introduced in 1993 to round out the bottom of the 55 series range.

Below: All the 55 series were available with a wide range of equipment. A mower is fitted here, which remained one of the most common tools used on these compact tractors.

Below: The bigger 955 with ROPS (Roll Over Protection System) and mower. Note the turf tires fitted, instead of the more aggressive treads of agricultural field tires.

5000 Series

The 5000 series marked something of a new era for John Deere. Not only was it the first of the "Thousand" series that would make up the company's range during the 1990s and early 21st century, but it was made in America. Through the '80s, it began to look as if the USA would never make small utility tractors again—it was simply cheaper to import them from Japan, Italy, Britain, or Germany, and all the mainstream US manufacturers did this.

However, in late 1991 John Deere announced the production of an all-new range of tractors, put together at an all-new factory in Augusta, Georgia. At first there were three of them, all powered by a three-cylinder 179ci (2.9 liter) diesel with bore and stroke dimensions of 4.19 x 4.33 inches, and rated at 2,400rpm: the 40 PTO hp 5200,

50hp 5300 and turbocharged 5400 with 60hp. Tests at Nebraska confirmed that John Deere's power claims were accurate (a little modest, if anything) and measured drawbar power at 35.9hp, 43.4hp, and 54.3hp for the three 5000s respectively.

Brand new US-built utility tractors would have been unthinkable a decade earlier but this production was something of a statement of faith in both American manufacturing and in a tractor market which had been in the doldrums for a decade.

Replacing the Mannheim-built 2155 and 2355, the new 5000s all had nine-speed transmissions, together with either a standard collar-shift unit or the optional top-shaft-synchronized version. None of them had cabs as standard, but there was fold-down ROPS, and front-

wheel-assist was also available as an extra option for those who wanted it.

The range was soon extended, with a narrow-tread 5400N for orchard/vineyard work added in 1994. The following year, the first four-cylinder 5000s appeared, the 70hp 5500 and narrow 5500N. And in 1996, the standard tractors finally gained a cab, with a narrower version built for the N series.

A couple of steps up from the 5000s were the 3055 and 3255, unveiled in 1992 as replacements for the 3155. Both were powered by a six-cylinder diesel of 359ci (5.9 liters) which came in natural aspirated form in the 3055 (90hp at the PTO) or as a turbo in the 3155 (100 PTO hp). The two tractors were two-wheel-drive and front-wheel-assist respectively.

Right: A great example of a 5400N. The "N" denotes a narrow tread, designed for narrow-spaced crops or orchard work, where space was at a premium.

Left: The turbocharged 60hp 5400 was top of the original 5000 line-up, this one with the optional cab and front implement hitch.

Below: For a while, many people predicted that no more small utility tractors would be made in the USA. The 5000 proved them wrong.

4560-4960

This was the last gasp for the big Waterloo row-crop tractors before their role was taken over by the bigger versions of the 7000 Series from 1993, and then by the all-new 8000 the following year. Engines, transmissions, and power ratings were unchanged (still 155-, 175-, and 200hp at the PTO) and the 4560, 4760, and 4960 replaced the 4555, 4755, and 4955 respectively.

In truth, there were very few changes changes (due to the fact that the tractors only had to be kept saleable for one more year) though visibility was improved by moving the air intake under the hood, and the muffler to the cab corner. Rack-and-pinion adjustment was reintroduced for the rear wheel tread and there were wider cab steps. Perhaps the most significant benefit for buyers was the introduction of a five-year warranty.

There was so little change that the 60 series row crops were never required to undergo another Nebraska test, and any figures may be taken from those of the 55 series, which would have been identical.

Meanwhile, John Deere's range of compact tractors had been supplanted back in 1986 with three new models built at the Horicon, Wisconsin factory. Although assembled in the US, these used three-cylinder Yanmar diesel engines, endowing the little 655 with 10.6hp at the PTO, the 755 with 15hp, and the 855 with 19hp. All three used hydrostatic drive.

These compact tractors were the only new launch from John Deere in the mid 1980s. This was hardly surprising because a lot of money had been spent on new launches in 1982, while major updates were on the drawing board for 1988/89. Adding further to its troubles, the company was losing money thanks to the slump in tractor sales, and John Deere also had a major strike on its hands in 1986/87. But after the strike ended in February, the company more than bounced back by making an impressive $315 million profit in 1988.

The smallest tractors were still sourced from Yanmar, though the range had now been been pruned to make way for the new Horicon-built 55 series. From 1989, the 650-1050 Yanmars were replaced by a new 70 series: the three-cylinder 18.5hp 670 and 28hp 870, and the four-cylinder 33hp 970 and 38.5hp 1070. All of these machines were produced as gear-driven tractors, unlike the hydrostatic, in-house machines.

Below: By the early 1990s, big row-crop tractors had settled on a standard format, regardless of who made them. Power came from a six-cylinder diesel of around 450ci, turbocharged and usually intercooled as well. Four-wheel-drive was standard, as was a large, roomy and comfortable cab, often with air conditioning. Transmission options usually consisted of partial or full power shift systems. John Deere's 7000 series, which replaced the 60 seen here, continued the tradition.

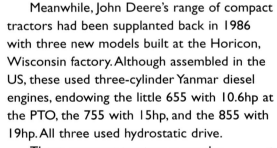

Above: Spot the differences with the 55 series (pages 114-115).
You'll do well to find more than a handful: easier cab access via
wider steps, and the air intake has disappeared under the hood
to improve visibility. What you can't see is the rack-and-pinion
wheel adjustment, and a five-year warranty.

6000 Series

The year 1992 saw one of John Deere's most significant launches ever. Simultaneously, in the fall of 1992, the Mannheim-built 6000 series and Waterloo-built 7000 were launched. Together, they replaced the larger Mannheim 55 series tractors as well as the Waterloo 60 series row-crops and would form the backbone of the John Deere range right through the 1990s into the 21st century.

Not since the launch of the New Generation, over 30 years before, had the company's future depended so much on a single new product. It was trumpeted as, "An All New Breed of Power," and for once the copy writers weren't overstating the case, as only a mere nine components had been carried over from the 60 series.

There were redesigned engines (all four-cylinder diesels on the early 6000s), new and more spacious cabs, and no less than three new transmissions. Under the skin, they were based on a new modular design with an independent steel main frame.

A lot of work had been done on this new generation of John Deere engines, which boasted an impressive torque rise of 35-38%. That brought constant horsepower as engine speed dropped from 2,100rpm to 1,700rpm. The range kicked off with the 6100, though this one wasn't sold in the USA, where the entry-level tractor was the 66 PTO hp 6200, powered by a 239ci (3.9 liter) four. The 6300 (75hp) used a turbocharged version of the same engine, while the 85hp 6400 housed a 276ci (4.5 liter) unit, this too turbocharged. These three tractors replaced the 2555, 2755, and 2955 respectively.

Front-wheel-assist was an option, and transmission choices started with a 12-speed SynchroPlus (three forward speeds in four ranges). There was also a 16-speed PowrQuad (four speeds in four ranges) and finally an impressive Power Shift, which allowed on-the-go shifting across 19 ratios. Another new feature that was increasingly common on 1990s tractors, was full suspension, in this case Triple Link Suspension, designed to improve on road handling and comfort. As standard, these were open platform tractors with foldable ROPS, but a new cab named ComfortGard (that was the US name—it was the less homely TechCentre in Europe) was an option. This had two-door access and reduced the noise level to around 75 dB(A).

The 6000 range soon began to grow. A low profile 6000L was added for orchards and vineyards, while extra-wide and high-clearance models were also offered. But the big news came in the year following the 6000's introduction, with the unveiling of more powerful six-cylinder models in 1993. The 110hp 6600 and 120hp 6800 came first, both of them with mechanical front-wheel-drive as standard. They were followed in 1994 by the 130hp 6900, and then the year after by the lower powered (it did without a turbo) 105hp 6506. The 6900 in particular was destined for great success, and as the updated 6910 would become Europe's best selling tractor in the late 1990s.

There were lots of updates and variations on the 6000 theme in the decade that followed its introduction. The mid-1990s saw more hard times in farming, so Deere launched the Task Masters: 6200 SE, 6400 SE, 6200L SE, and 6400L SE. These featured the basic SynchroPlus transmission and were all less expensive than the standard models. In the US, the 6005 Advantage series did much the same job from 1997, including an 85hp 6405 and 95hp 6605, with two-wheel-drive or MFWD.

The entire range was updated as the 6010 in 1998, which meant that there was more power right across the range, apart from the turbo-less 6510 (which replaced the 6506). In 2001, the range got another update as the 6020 series, in both four- and six-cylinder form. Now extending up to 160hp for the top tractor, the 6000 overlapped the Waterloo-built 7000 to some degree, though this was intentional.

There were more engine changes, with Dual Temperature Cooling and a Charge Air Cooler, plus extra

Above: In some ways, the new 6000/7000 series were just as big a deal for John Deere as the New Generation of 1960 had been—they were almost all-new.

Right: The steel main frame of the 6000 series tractor is shown clearly in this plan carrying the engine, transmission, rear axle, and three-point hitch.

power for all the six-cylinder 6000s. The fours too were creeping up the power range—the entry-level 6000 now offered 80hp, and there was a new 6420S with 120hp. Another new feature was AutoPowr, which allowed road speeds of up to 31mph, and the option of hydraulic cab suspension on certain models.

The 6000 series had proved to be another real winner for John Deere, building a very good reputation and selling in large numbers.

SPECIFICATIONS

John Deere 6300

Engine type Four-cylinder turbo, water-cooled

Fuel type Diesel

Bore x stroke 4.19 x 4.33in

Capacity 239ci (3.9 liters)

Rated speed 2,300rpm

TRANSMISSION

Transmission type Partial power shift

Speeds 16F

Speed range 1.5-18.4mph

Factory weight 9,645lb

PERFORMANCE

Power (at PTO) 76.0hp

Power (at drawbar) 62.1hp

Fuel efficiency (PTO) 17.10hp/hr per gallon

Cab noise 73.5 dB(A)

John Deere 6400

Engine type Four-cylinder turbo, water-cooled

Fuel type Diesel

Bore x stroke 4.19 x 5.00in

Capacity 276ci (4.5 liters)

Rated speed 2,300rpm

TRANSMISSION

Transmission type Partial power shift

Speeds 16F

Speed range 1.5-19.0mph

Factory weight 10,285lb

PERFORMANCE

Power (at PTO) 85.2hp

Power (at drawbar) 76.6hp

Fuel efficiency (PTO) 17.52hp/hr per gallon

Cab noise 74.5 dB(A)

Above: The 6000 laid bare. The complexity of a modern tractor transmission is obvious here, and a new option was the 19-speed full power shift, allowing on the move shifting across the whole range.

Above: Initially, there were three 6000s for the USA: 6200 (66hp), 6300 (75hp), and 6400 (85hp).

JOHN DEERE

6400

7000 Series

John Deere 7600 (1993)

Engine type Six-cylinder turbo, water-cooled

Fuel type Diesel

Bore x stroke 4.19 x 5.00in

Capacity 414ci (6.7 liters)

Rated speed 2,100rpm

TRANSMISSION

Transmission type Power Shift

Speeds 19F

Speed range 0.9-22.8mph

Factory weight 15,116lb

PERFORMANCE

Power (at PTO) 111.6hp

Power (at drawbar) 93.5hp

Fuel efficiency (PTO) 17.53hp/hr per gallon

Cab noise 72.0 dB(A)

JOHN DEERE 7800

Engine type Six-cylinder turbo, water-cooled

Fuel type Diesel

Bore x stroke 4.56 x 4.75in

Capacity 466ci (7.6 liters)

Rated speed 2,100rpm

TRANSMISSION

Transmission type Power Shift

Speeds 19F

Speed range 1.0-24.2mph

Factory weight 15,560lb

PERFORMANCE

Power (at PTO) 146.7hp

Power (at drawbar) 135.6hp

Fuel efficiency (PTO) 17.1hp/hr per gallon

Cab noise 72.5 dB(A)

So while Mannheim was busy building its high-tech, good-selling 6000 series, what was happening at Waterloo, where John Deeres had been built for over 70 years? The answer was the 7000 series. It had much in common with the 6000, built on the same modular system, and both ranges had been designed and launched simultaneously, to complement each other.

So while the first 6000s were all four-cylinder tractors covering the 66-85hp range, the three new six-cylinder 7000s started at 110 PTO hp with the 7600, included the 125hp 7700, and finally the 145hp 7800. All three used a John Deere-built six-cylinder turbocharged diesel—417ci (6.8 liters) for the 7600 and 466ci (7.6 liters) for the other two. They replaced the 4055, 4255, and 4455 respectively. As with the 6000, there was great emphasis on the torque rise, which in this case was 38%.

Other features were very similar to those of the 6000—the optional ComfortGard cab and the choice of a 16-speed PowrQuad or 19-speed Power Shift transmission. There was a choice of two-wheel-drive or MFWD, the ComfortGard cab or open platform ROPS and Triple Link Suspension.

And as with the 6000, the range was rapidly extended once the first three models had gone to market. As they launched, there was a big power gap between the top 6000 tractor and lowest-powered 7000, so as the 6000 went upmarket with six-cylinders, the 7000s extended downwards to meet them. In 1993, a 92 PTO hp 7200 and 100hp 7400 were launched to help bridge the gap.

Three years later, the 7000 got its first major update as the 7010, a major part of this was the new PowrTech engine. This 417ci (6.8 liter) unit was developed to meet tougher emissions regulations, which were coming into play on both sides of the Atlantic. Thanks to electronic injection control, it did that and produced more power than the old engine into the bargain.

Just as economy versions of 6000 were launched to help John Deere through a depressed marketplace, so it was with the 7000. The 7005 Advantage was launched in 1997, including a 105hp 7405 which came in standard or high-clearance form. The following year, the big 7710 and 7810 were up-engined with a 497ci (8.1 liter) version of the PowrTech, which came straight out of the new 8000 series. Again, the company was playing mix and match with components to ensure a healthy overlap between tractor ranges, and leaving no niche unfilled.

SPECIFICATIONS: JOHN DEERE 7700

Engine type	Six-cylinder turbo, water-cooled
Fuel type	Diesel
Bore x stroke	4.56 x 4.75in
Capacity	466ci (7.6 liters)
Rated speed	2,100rpm
Transmission type	Power Shift
Speeds	19F
Speed range	1.0-24.2mph
Factory weight	15,506lb
Power (at PTO)	126.1hp
Power (at drawbar)	113.3hp
Fuel efficiency	16.41hp/hr per gallon
Cab noise	72.5 dB(A)

Left: The 7000 was Waterloo's all-new tractor for the 1990s, complementing the 6000 series tractors that were produced in the Mannheim factory.

Above: The ComfortGard cab was a big attraction of the 7800. Since the SoundGard of 1972, John Deere had been at the forefront of cab design.

Below: Four-wheel-drive on this 7800, a feature fast becoming standard on 100hp+ machines.

8570-8970

SPECIFICATIONS

John Deere 8570 (1993)

Engine type Six-cylinder turbo-intercooled, water-cooled

Fuel type Diesel

Bore x stroke 4.56 x 4.75in

Capacity 466ci (7.6 liters)

Rated speed 2,100rpm

Transmission type Partial power shift

Speeds 24F

Speed range 2.0-21.2mph

Factory weight 32,265lb

Power (at PTO) 208.2hp

Power (at drawbar) 191.6hp

Fuel efficiency (PTO) 17.46hp/hr per gallon

Fuel effiency (drawbar) 15.23hp/hr per gallon

Cab noise 74.0 dB(A)

JOHN DEERE 8970 (1993)

Engine Type Six-cylinder turbo, water-cooled

Fuel type Diesel

Bore x stroke 5.50 x 6.00in

Capacity 855ci (13.9 liters)

Rated speed 2,100rpm

Transmission type Partial power shift

Speeds 24F

Speed range 2.1-22.1mph

Factory weight 33,820lb

Power (at PTO) 354.5hp

Power (at drawbar) 313.9hp

Fuel efficiency (PTO) 17.1hp/hr per gallon

Fuel efficiency (drawbar) 14.66hp/hr per gallon

Cab noise 74.0 dB(A)

The final update for the "8000" super-tractors came early in 1993, when John Deere announced the 70 series, now up to four models, all of them with more power than before.

Replacing the 200 PTO hp 8560 as lead-in tractor was the 8570, still using that faithful 466ci (7.6 liter) six-cylinder turbo-diesel, now uprated slightly to give 208hp at the PTO, which translated into 250hp at the flywheel.

Another John Deere engine, the 619ci (10.1 liter) six with turbo and intercooler, powered the next two tractors. In the 8770, power was up by a modest 3hp, to 259hp at the PTO, but for the new 8870 it was boosted to 302 PTO hp and 350hp at the flywheel. In other words, about the same as the top-range Cummins of the previous year, or for that matter, John Deere's own 955ci (15.6 liter) V8 of 1982. All these engines used electronic injection, which improved power, efficiency, and cut emissions, while also boosting the torque rise between 2,100rpm and 1,900rpm.

To make room for this hopped-up John Deere powered 70 series, the Cummins engined super-tractor (now named 8970) offered 354hp at the PTO and a claimed 400 at the flywheel. As ever, it was the largest, most powerful John Deere ever made. When tested by Nebraska, the 8970 weighed in at 33,820lb—actually less than the lower powered 8870. It could also muster almost 314hp at the drawbar, while the smaller 70 series offered 192hp, 243hp and 280hp respectively.

Below: With up to 354hp at the PTO and over 400 at the flywheel, the final 8000 series super-tractors were capable of hauling impressive loads.

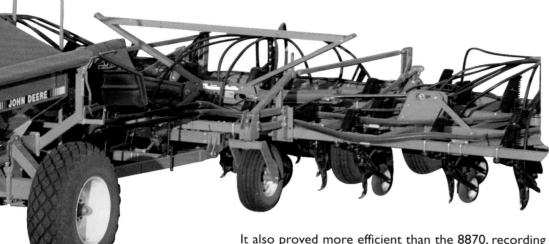

It also proved more efficient than the 8870, recording 17.1hp/hr per gallon at maximum PTO power, and 14.66 on a ten-hour drawbar run at 75% power. This Nebraska fuel figure was a measure, not of outright fuel consumption, but of work done per gallon of diesel—that is, overall efficiency.

It was thus a real guide to the true economics of giant super-tractors. They might cost six-figure sums to buy, and guzzle fuel at an alarming rate, but in terms of work done in time available, they often proved more economical than smaller ones. The Cummins 70 series was respectably efficient in this regard, continuing the John Deere tradition, though the best of the range was actually the smallest—the 8570 managed 17.46hp/hr per gallon on Nebraska's PTO test, 15.23 on the drawbar.

Once again, there was a choice of three transmissions for the John Deere super-tractors. The standard 12-speed unit gave three synchronized speeds in four ranges; an optional 2-speed Power Shift doubled that into a 24-speed; or you could opt for a full 12-speed Power Shift, though only on the three larger machines. Other options included a three-point hitch (except for the 8970), a PTO, and triple tires. One interesting new feature was Field Cruise Control, which enabled the tractor to maintain a constant ground speed during seeding or light tillage.

Below: Huge, and hugely expensive, yet the big super-tractors made economic sense for big farms that could afford them.

2000/3000 Series

In the early 1990s, John Deere needed a relatively low-cost tractor to sell in markets like Argentina, South Africa, and Mexico. Machines built at Waterloo, Dubuque, or Mannheim were simply too expensive, but it found the answer—two of them in fact—within Europe. In late 1993 a deal was signed with Zetor of the Czech Republic.

A maker of good-value tractors in Eastern Europe, Zetor had been working hard to survive in a post-Cold War world. The company had lost its guaranteed markets in the former Communist states, but could now offer low-cost tractors from Europe that were ideal for Deere stable of machines.

So the John Deere 2000 Series announced in 1993 was no more than a rebadged Zetor. The range comprised a single three-cylinder tractor, the 49hp 2000, but the rest were fours. Of these, only one (the 62hp 2100) was naturally aspirated—the others were all turbocharged. These were the 81hp 2400, 89hp 2700, 100hp 2800, and 106hp 2900. These tractors ran through to 1999.

Renault of France also offered competitively priced machines, and the same year as it signed the deal with Zetor, John Deere began selling Renault tractors, repainted and badged to suit. However, they were not pure Renaults, using John Deere engines from the company's French plant at Saran.

The initial series range consisted of the 55hp three-cylinder 3100 and four-cylinder 65hp 3200/3300 plus 85hp turbocharged 3400. Higher specification X Series were offered later. The X cab offered a digital display and multi-function console, plus under-hood exhaust, front fenders, Walterscheid hook end, and a 145 liter fuel tank.

The 3000s looked modern and up to the minute, with their low, sloping noses and glassy two-door cabs, which combined to give fine visibility. There were two transmission options, both with a shuttle reverser as standard, reflecting the 3000's role as an all-round utility tractor. The standard 20-speed (forward or reverse) featured a mechanical splitter, but the X series brought Twinshift—full Power Shift, in other words. A 540/1,000rpm PTO was standard, with hydraulic-assist PTO engagement on the X series.

From 1996 two new 3000 series models—the 75hp 3300SE and 85hp 3400SE—aimed to offer lower priced tractors at a fixed specification. These models still had the option of the up-spec X cab and hydrostatic steering. In 1998, the entire 3000 series was updated as the 3010—sound familiar?

Confusing for tractor historians, though of course the latest 3010 was very different from the original New Generation 3010 of 1960.

Below: John Deere 3000s of the 1990s were really rebadged Renaults, albeit with Deere power units.

Above: Standard transmission on the 3000 series was a
20-speed (forward or reverse) with mechanical splitter, but
a full power shift (named Twinshift) soon followed, with
the higher tech X series.

Below: The 85 horsepower 3400 was top model of the 3000s,
coming with a turbocharged four-cylinder engine. It was later
available as both high spec X series or price-cutting SE.

8000 Series

SPECIFICATIONS

John Deere 8100 (1996)

Engine type Six-cylinder turbo-intercooled, water-cooled

Fuel type Diesel

Bore x stroke 4.63 x 5.14in

Capacity 496ci (8.1 liters)

Rated speed 2,200rpm

Transmission type Power Shift

Speeds 16F/5R

Speed range 1.4-23.8mph

Factory weight n/a

Power (at PTO) 185hp

Torque 815Nm

Torque reserve 40.9%

Tire size F 16.9 R 30

Tire size R 20.8 R 42

Fuel capacity 511 liters

Hitch lift 7,933kg

Cab noise 74.0 dB(A)

JOHN DEERE 8400 (1996)

Engine type Six-cylinder turbo-intercooled, water-cooled

Fuel type Diesel

Bore x stroke 4.63 x 5.14in

Capacity 496ci (8.1 liters)

Rated speed 2,200rpm

Transmission type Power Shift

Speeds 16F/5R

Speed range 1.4-23.8mph

Factory weight n/a

Power (at PTO) 260hp

Torque 179Nm

Torque reserve 40.5%

Tire size F 16.9 R 30

Tire size R 20.8 R 42

Fuel capacity 511 liters

Hitch lift 8,882kg

John Deere's big row-crop tractors from Waterloo, the 55 and 60 series, were replaced by two ranges. The smaller 55s were superseded by the new 7000 Series in 1993, while the bigger row-crops received a final 60 series update in 1992, before being replaced by the all-new 8000 Series two years later.

Ranging from 160hp to 225hp, these two-wheel-drive tractors offered the sort of power that only ten years before had been the sole preserve of giant four-wheel-drive machines. Front-wheel-assist was standard on the top model though, and optional on the other three. Those three continued to use John Deere's 466ci (7.6 liter) six-cylinder diesel, now with aftercooling as well as turbocharging. The base model 8100 offered 160hp at the PTO and replaced the 4560. The 8200 (180hp) did the same job for the 4760, while the 8300 (200hp) was the 4960's replacement.

But a new model and engine took the 8000 up into a new power class. The range-topping 8400 was powered by a new 496ci (8.1 liter) six-cylinder diesel, coupled also with a turbo and aftercooling. Bore and stroke measured 4.56 x 5.06 inches (the odd fractions betraying that John Deere was finally going metric) but the 8400 was not tested at Nebraska, so the figure of 225hp at the PTO is John Deere's estimate. Electronic injection control helped the new engine achieve a torque rise of 38% and a power rise of 10%. It was so successful that the company soon used fuelled-down versions of this unit in the 8100/8200/8300, pensioning off the long-serving 466.

The 8000 was quite different from its predecessor. The engine was moved forward 44 inches and raised ten inches to give more front wheel clearance for tight turns, plus better visibility. Visibility was also improved by a smaller dash, narrower hood and wider windscreen—the

CommandView cab had 62% more space than before, according to its maker. The instrumentation was relocated onto a large right-hand console (to allow that narrower dash) and the major controls were found on the right-hand armrest.

The transmission was new too, a 16-speed full Power Shift which offered a range of 1.4-23.8mph on all four models. Like the four-wheel-drive 8000s (soon to be renamed to avoid confusion) Field Cruise Control was available enabling the tractor to automatically keep up a set ground speed.

Below: An all-new 496ci (8.1 liter) six-cylinder diesel powered the top of the range 8400—this engine would soon be used across the range.

Above: Rubber tracks were a new innovation for the 1990s, as many manufacturers followed Caterpiller's pioneering work.

Below: With up to 225hp (at the PTO) the 8000 took a row-crop tractor right up into super-tractor territory.

9000 Series

SPECIFICATIONS

John Deere 9400 (1996)

Engine type Six-cylinder turbo-intercooled, water-cooled

Fuel type Diesel

Bore x stroke 5.00 x 6.50in

Capacity 767ci (12.5 liters)

Rated speed 2,100rpm

TRANSMISSION

Transmission type Synchro

Speeds 12F

Options 24F PowrSync, 12F Power Shift

Factory weight 37,000lb (16,798kg)

Power (at PTO) 425hp

MISCELLANEOUS

Track widths (9400T) 30in (36in optional)

Hitch type Category 3 or 4/4N

For nearly a decade John Deere had been dependent on Cummins to power its largest, most powerful tractor, dropping its own 955ci (15.6 liter) V8 in favour of a smaller Cummins six. But with the launch of the 9000 Series in 1996, which replaced the 60 series as the company's flagship four-wheel-drive tractor, it once again offered a complete range of in-house power units.

The entry-level 9100 was powered by the 496ci (8.1 liter) unit that had debuted in the 8400 tractor two years previously, and which was used by the updated 8010 across the range. Here it was in 260hp form, putting a clear gap between the "smallest" (these terms are relative) super-tractor and largest two-wheel-drive.

There were three other parts to the new 9000 range, and all of them used a variation of John Deere's new PowerTech engine, which was built at the Waterloo factory. All were six-cylinder turbocharged diesels, with air-to-air intercoolers. In fact, the six-cylinder diesel was becoming the standard format for almost every 100hp+

tractor in the world. In the 1970s and '80s, many manufacturers had used V8 diesels in their larger machines, but in the end, the straight-six proved more suitable. Being narrower, it did not interfere with visibility as a V8 did; electronic injection made it acceptably smooth and refined, while engine speeds rarely rose above 2,500rpm so six large and relatively heavy pistons in place of eight smaller ones were not necessarily a hindrance.

PowerTech came in two sizes: a 544ci (10.5 liter) unit of 310hp, fitted to the 9200, and a 767ci (12.5 liter) version, which came in 360hp form for the 9300 and 425hp for the 9400.

To go with the new engines, the 9000s offered three transmissions, the standard unit being the 12-speed Synchro, with three synchronised speeds in each of the four ranges. A 24-speed PowerSynch was optional, with

Below: John Deere badged, and John Deere powered as well—the big 9000 forsook Cummins diesels for Waterloo's homegrown variety.

partial power shifting. Finally, buyers could pay the extra for a full Power Shift 12-speed transmission.

Some features from the 8000 two-wheel-drive reappeared on this tractor, such as the more spacious CommandView cab and CommandArm module that swivelled with the seat. The latter, incidentally, was now called "ComfortCommand"—someone in the John Deere marketing department must have been in the military, or else had an authority fixation.

Electronics were now a vital part of high-tech tractors and the 9000 offered the option of the Field Office. This would store data from a day's work (fuel used, acreage covered, and so on) and could be plugged into a laptop computer. In the old days, tractor drivers took a bag of sandwiches with them for a day's work in the fields. Now, as well as lunch, he or she took a lap top. Like the 8000, the 9000 was later available with rubber tracks, and the 9300T and 9400T were launched in 1998.

Above right: Twin wheels front and rear on this 9300, but if that still wasn't enough traction, buyers could opt for the rubber-tracked "T".

Below: Big tractors cost big money, but they could pull massive implements, doing more work in less time.

7010

SPECIFICATIONS

John Deere 7220 (2003)

Engine type Six-cylinder turbo, water-cooled

Fuel type Diesel

Capacity 417ci (6.8 liters)

Rated speed 2,300rpm

TRANSMISSION

Transmission type PowrQuad-Plus

Speeds 16F/16R

Option 24-speed PowrQuad-Plus

DIMENSIONS

Factory weight 11,200lb

Wheelbase 112.8in

Hitch Category 2

PERFORMANCE

Power (at PTO) 95hp

Power (at flywheel) 110hp

Hydraulic pressure 2,900psi

Noise (in cab) 72dB(A)

Despite the huge advance of the 7000 series, it was of course impossible for John Deere to stand still, so three years on the tractor was updated as the 7010 series. The centerpiece of this was a new six-cylinder diesel named PowrTech. It wasn't that the 7000 had been lacking in power, more that the old-generation engine simply could not meet the new wave of emissions legislation in the USA and Europe.

The PowrTech was a 417ci (6.8 liter) unit, and its secret weapon, one being increasingly adopted by diesel engines to clean up their act, was electronic injection control. This allowed far more precise control of the injection process, producing a more complete fuel burn and cutting the amount of particulates and unburnt hydrocarbons that appeared out of the tractor's exhaust pipe as black smoke.

At first PowrTech only came in the lower powered 7010 tractors, but in 1997 a larger 497ci (8.1 liter) version was fitted to the 7700 and 7800, which were rebadged 7710 and 7810 to suit. This bigger PowrTech was almost identical to that fitted to the big 8000 series John Deeres.

Just like the original 7000, the 7010 made great use of electronics, but in a quite unobtrusive way. The 7000 was not perceived as a particularly high-tech tractor, but under the skin it was right up to date. At the heart of it was the data BUS system, an electronic wiring loom linking several "intelligent" components. These comprised of the dashboard, hitch control box, the transmission control on powershift models, a single socket to programme the system and diagnose faults, and a Basic Control Module, which housed controls for various other functions. There was also an optional performance monitor. Although an integrated system, it would keep working even if one of the components failed.

Unusually the entire system was designed and built by John Deere itself—many manufacturers preferred to buy-in their electronics. So the Headland Management System (HMS) was unique to John Deere. This greatly simplified headland turns, with a phased switching off of the diff locks, PTO, and four-wheel-drive as the implement was raised, and automatically switching them back on after the turn was made and the implement was lowered again. No one could accuse John Deere of lagging behind technically. (Please note that the specifications on this page are for the latest update of the 7000 series, the 7220.)

Below: A spotless 7610, hitched up to an equally spotless trailer. Big news with the 10 series update was the new PowrTech diesel.

Below right: The 7010 series made great use of electronics, with an integrated system linking the hitch control, power shift transmission, and other functions.

Below: John Deere's Headland Management System automatically switched off the diff locks, PTO, and four-wheel-drive when the implement was raised, thus easing headland turns.

4000 Series

It was a sign of the times that compact tractors were once again being built in the United States. Japanese tractors had become relatively expensive and so when the time came to replace the sub-40hp Yanmar-sourced 70 series in 1997, it was with a John Deere-built tractor, though the new 4000 Series still used a Yanmar engine.

Rolling off the production line at JD's Augusta, Georgia factory, the 4000 replaced Deere's own hydrostatic 55 series as well as the gear-driven Yanmars. In a nod to the past, John Deere referred to the 4000s as a "new generation" and they kicked off with the 20-engine hp 4100, which replaced the 18.5hp 670 and was powered by a Yanmar three-cylinder diesel. Even on this, the cheapest model of the range, an eight-speed forward/four-reverse transmission was standard, along with on-the-move engagement of front-wheel-drive, a differential lock and hydrostatic power steering. There was a choice of gear or hydrostatic drive.

It was joined the following year by four extra models, from the 21.5hp (at the PTO) 4200 to the 36hp 4600. In 2000, the range was topped off by the 4700, with 38.5hp. Many options were offered for these general purpose tractors, with turf tires being popular for golf course and garden use. They could also be equipped with a well specified cab for use in all weathers and items like a front loader and PowrReverser to turn the 4000 into a mini yard tractor.

Below: Mower-equipped 4400, with ROPS—like all the 4000s, this was built by John Deere but powered by Yanmar.

JOHN DEERE 4010 MODEL RANGE - 2003

Model	Power	Chassis
4010	18hp	Small
4110	20hp	Small
4115	24hp	Small
4210	28hp	Mid
4310	32hp	Mid
4410	35hp	Mid
4510	39hp	Large
4610	44hp	Large
4710	48hp	Large

Left: This attractive, spacious, and glassy cab was an option on the 4000 series—why should garden workers be denied weather protection?

Below: A well optioned 4100, with cab, front loader, and mower, turning the basic lawn tractor into a maid of all work.

5010/5100

SPECIFICATIONS

John Deere 5103 (2003)

Engine type Three-cylinder, water-cooled

Fuel type Diesel

Capacity 179ci (2.9 liters)

Rated speed 2,400rpm

TRANSMISSION

Transmission type Sliding gear

Speeds 9F/3R

DIMENSIONS

Factory weight 4,475lb

Wheelbase 80.7in

Tread width F 57-62.3in

Tread width R 55.8-71.7in

Tire size F 7.5 x 16

Tire size R 3.6 x 28

Hitch Category I or II

PERFORMANCE

Power (at PTO) 38hp

Power (at flywheel) 44hp

Turn radius 116.4in

Hydraulics max pressure 2,828psi

In 1998, the Augusta-built 5000 series received its first major update as the 5010. Two smaller tractors were added, both with three-cylinder engines, while the four-cylinder 5410 and 5510 turbo both had a power boost of 5hp. That was for the US range—there were still variations for the European market, though now all based on the same model of tractor. Europeans had their own 5010 update in 2002, with both markets had the option of narrow-section orchard N models, which came in narrow and super-narrow widths.

In 2002, American buyers received the upgraded 20 series, which by the following year comprised of nine models—four 20 series and five lower powered 03/05 series. The latest range began with the 5103, powered by the same 178ci (2.9 liter) three-cylinder wet-liner diesel used by the original 5000s, here delivering 38hp at the PTO, 44hp at the flywheel, at 2,400rpm. One change was that it could now run on a part-mix of biodiesel, the diesel fuel substitute derived from rapeseed oil.

There was still a nine-speed transmission, with three reverse ratios, and the 5103 had the option of two-wheel-drive or mechanical front-wheel-drive. Hydrostatic power steering was standard, as was a differential lock. There were oil-cooled disc brakes (claimed by Deere to offer better durability), open center hydraulics, a Category I or II three-point hitch, plus independent 540rpm PTO. All of this technology meant it added up to quite a sophisticated little tractor.

Right: The 10 series represented the first update on the Atlanta-built 5000 tractors, but bigger changes came in 2002 when the range split in two: the higher spec 20 series and lower powered 03/05 series.

The rest of the range followed even power steps upwards. One up from the 5103, the 5105 offered 45hp at the flywheel, as a two-wheel-drive open platform tractor. The 5105 was a 53hp equivalent, with standard four-wheel-drive. The 5203 also offered 53hp and the 5303 64hp—both used the same 178ci triple, the 5303 in turbocharged form. Four-cylinder 20 series 5000s comprised the 53hp 5220, 64hp 5320 81hp 5420, and 89hp 5520. Like every other John Deere range, the 5000 utility tractors had expanded upwards as the years went by and patriots could breathe a sigh of relief—they really were "Made in America."

Left: A front loader was a popular option and the 5000 series was a popular yard tractor. This is the range topping 5510.

Below: This is the narrow-tread 5310, designed specifically to squeeze down between lines of orchard trees or through a vineyard. Note forward-mounted ROPS.

8010

For 2000, John Deere's biggest two-wheel-drive tractors became the 8010, their first major update. But "two-wheel-drive" was becoming something of a misnomer. For one thing, the top-range 8400 had front-wheel-assist as standard from the original launch—this system, increasingly common on modern high-horsepower tractors, was a half-way house towards full four-wheel-drive. And for another, from June 1997 the 8000 had been available with rubber tracks. Technically, it was still a two-wheel-drive tractor, with two rear wheels driving the tracks, but in practice it was a crawler by any other name.

Caterpillar, the best known name in crawlers worldwide, had pioneered rubber tracks for agricultural tractors back in 1986. The idea was to combine the superb traction and low ground impaction of tracks with greater maneuverability and higher road speeds. If not the best of both worlds (rubber tires and steel tracks) then a workable compromise. In any case it was a success, and the original Caterpillar Challenger spawned a whole range of machines, taking the crawler manufacturer into direct competition with the John Deere 8000 and 9000 series.

It was only a matter of time before the mainstream tractor makers came up with their own rubber-tracked

Above: The rubber track option was effective but expensive, and in any case, the top 8400 already offered front-wheel-assist as standard.

machines, and in fact John Deere was one of the first. When it arrived, the 8000T, as it was known, was the first tracked John Deere since the much smaller 2010 of the 1960s. To the outsider, it looked quite similar to the Caterpillar Challenger 35/45. Caterpillar thought so too. So much so, that they immediately filed a lawsuit against John Deere after the 8000Ts first public appearance. "Our tractors are gaining popularity because of their unique design that provides numerous advantages to the farmer," said Caterpillar vice-president Dick Benson at the time. "We intend to aggressively protect our patented designs from others who would infringe them."

Lawsuit or not, when the updated 8010 was launched for 2000, it came with a track option. There was also an extra 5-10hp across the range, depending on model, and the new Implement Management System, which enabled the driver to control up to 12 different functions of tractor and implement, simultaneously.

As for the tracks, they were optional on all four 10 series 8000s, from an 8010T to an 8410T. Tracks apart, these tractors were very similar to their wheeled equivalents. John Deere retained a twin-wheel option though, for those farmers who needed more traction than the standard single-wheel set up could provide but didn't want, or couldn't afford, the full rubber track treatment.

Below: A 8210T with the rubber tracks that Caterpillar claimed John Deere had copied from its own design. But Deere wasn't the only manufacturer following Caterpillar in building rubber-tracked field tractors.

JOHN DEERE 8000/8010

Model	Production Dates
8000	1994-1999
8000T	1997-1999
8010	2000-2001
8010T	2000-2001
8020	2001 to present
8020T	2001 to present

3200-3800 Telehandlers

SPECIFICATIONS

John Deere 3800 (2002)

Engine type Four-cylinder turbo, water-cooled

Fuel Diesel

Capacity 278ci (4.5 liters)

TRANSMISSION

Transmission type Power shift + torque converter

Speeds 5F/3R (reverse shuttle)

Speed range Up to 21.9mph

DIMENSIONS

Height 109in

Length 218.6in

Width 89.2in

Factory weight 14,520lb

Tire size F 15.5/80 x 24

Tire size R 15.5/80 x 24

Fuel capacity 130 liters

PERFORMANCE

Power (at flywheel) 117hp

Loader capacity 5,500lb

Loader max height 212in

Loader rotation 166 degrees

Turn radius 166.8in

John Deere has long been a multi-product company. In the early days, tractors were just one product of many wearing the John Deere badge. Nearly a century later, the same holds true—as well as farm tractors, the company makes a huge range of implements, construction equipment, and ride-on or walk-behind lawn mowers. But it took Deere a while to recognise the niche market of telehandlers—basically super-duty forklifts, used for shuffling around farm yards, loading grain, or stacking hay. Farmers in the United States preferred small utility tractors for this work.

But the market was growing, especially in Europe, and John Deere responded by selling the Northern Irish-built Matbro (a pioneer of this field) in John Deere colors and badging, from 1998. The engines came from Deere's own plant in Saran, France. Three models were available: 92hp 4350, 100hp 4450, and 4550. But it's always cheaper in the

Above: The flourishing market for telehandlers in Europe encouraged John Deere to launch its own in 2000, after two years of selling rebadged, re-engined Matbros.

long-run to build things yourself (especially for a company the size of John Deere) and in 2000 the company announced its own range of in-house telehandlers, built at Zwebrucken, Germany.

The new 3200 and 3400 used the same four-cylinder turbocharged diesel of 100hp, the difference being that the 3400 could lift heavier loads, and stack them higher. The engine was straight out of the Deere field tractor range, but the transmission was quite different in order to suit the conditions of yard work. The requirements here weren't for multiple ratios, but quick and easy shifting between forward and reverse, so the Deere telehandlers

Above: Another benefit of telehandlers was that they freed up more powerful conventional tractors for fieldwork.

Below: Adaptability is the telehandler's forte, as much at home stacking bales out in the field as it is shunting in the yard.

used a torque converter, mated to a Turner five-speed (in either direction) Power Shift with reverse shuttle.

Within the relatively small telehandler market, a debate rages about the relative merits of rigid chassis and pivot-steer machines. Rigid chassis' are less maneuverable than pivot-steerers, and visibility tends to be less open, but they can generally cope with heavier loads and lift them higher—typically 3 tonnes up to 7 meters, against 2.5 tonnes up to 5 meters.

But where maneuverability is all, as in smaller yards, that is thought a price worth paying by some customers—hence in 2002 the 3700 and 3800 telehandlers, able to pivot through 45 degrees for a very tight turning circle, with fine visibility and an automatic side-shift. Power came from a choice of 97hp (3700) or 110hp (3800) 276ci (4.5 litre) four-cylinder turbo-diesels. Yet again, for John Deere, another niche was filled.

8020

SPECIFICATIONS

John Deere 8520 (2002)

Engine type Six-cylinder turbo-intercooled, water-cooled

Fuel type Diesel

Bore x stroke 4.63 x 5.14in

Capacity 496ci (8.1 liters)

Rated speed 2,400rpm

TRANSMISSION

Transmission type Power Shift

Speeds 16F/5r

Speed range Up to 26.3mph

DIMENSIONS

Factory weight n/a

Tested weight n/a

Wheelbase n/a

Tire size F n/a

Tire size R Up to 710/70 R 42

Fuel capacity 606 liters

Track widths 18in, 24in or 31.3in

PERFORMANCE

Power (rated) 295hp

Power (max) 325hp

Torque rise 43%

Power rise 13%

Hitch lift 11 tonnes

Suspension had been a long time coming to tractors, but two things made it both necessary and possible. Higher road speeds and the need to maintain traction in the field (along with ever higher power and weight) made it highly desirable. Secondly, modern electronic control made it possible as well.

This was the biggest step forward for the John Deere 8020 series, announced in early 2002. John Deere's Triple Link Suspension had already appeared on the two-wheel-drive 6010 and 7010, but for the 8020 a completely new system—Independent Link Suspension—was developed.

Although based around a mechanical system of upper and lower control arms, with hydraulic cylinders, it was electronics that made the whole system work. A central computer monitored the axle position, compared this with what the tractor was doing at the time, decided how the suspension should react and sent the appropriate demand—all of this, many times a second. The result of all this technology was to keep the wheels perpendicular to the ground and in contact with it, thus improving traction as well as smoothing the ride. In England, the ILS option (front end only) cost £7,800—a rear-end equivalent was close to being launched.

As if that weren't enough, 8020 customers could also pay extra for something called the Active Seat. For £2,735, this suspended the operator's seat by a combination of air suspension and electro-hydraulics. Like the ILS down below, it was all controlled by computer, which in this case checked the seat position 200 times every second. According to journalist Charlene Finck, who test drove an 8020 with both seat and suspension for *Profi* magazine, the new systems, "offer a ride that glides over bumps and rough terrain with the operator barely moving."

There were five 8020s available, four of them with a rubber track option, so it looked as if the Caterpillar lawsuit hadn't stopped John Deere in its tracks (sic) after all. All were powered by the latest version of John Deere's 5.0 liter PowerTech diesel, with high-pressure common rail electronic injection, a turbocharger and air/air intercooler. Torque rise was an impressive 43%.

The lowest powered model was now the 8120 (rated at 200hp) followed by the 225hp 8220 and 250hp 8320. The range topped out with the 270hp 8420 and 295hp 8520. The first two had a maximum rear lift of 9.5 tonnes, the latter three of 11 tonnes (10 tonnes for the T tracked versions). Whichever way you looked at, the latest generation of 8000 series John Deeres were heavy duty tractors with a huge array of technology.

Above: For the first time, the 8020 offered Independent Link Suspension as an option, giving independent movement of the front wheels, with benefits in traction and comfort.

Left: This 8520T has the tracks set wide—a variety of widths were available.

Below: All 8020s were powered by John Deere's 5.0 liter Power Tech diesel, now with common rail injection.

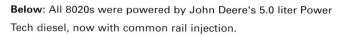

9020

More power, more sophistication, and a transmission that could think for itself summed up the 21st century version of the big 9000 series, announced in the summer of 2002. Although the PowerTech engines were uprated again, with 450hp on tap for the 9520, interest centered around the all-new Power Shift transmission.

With 18 forward speeds and four reverse it clearly offered more ratios than the old 12-speed, but its real advances lay behind the figures, and once again electronic control was making a whole range of new features possible. In the words of one journalist, it could "talk" to the engine, "politely requesting extra grunt to ensure a smooth shift from one gear to the next."

Being able to think for itself, the transmission would automatically select the most efficient gear out in the field, whatever the conditions. All the operator had to do was set a few parameters (maximum gear, desired throttle position, engine speed, and load) and the transmission did the rest. If the soil got sticky, it would automatically downshift, changing up again when the going got easier. Other little features were built in as well:

a clutchless power shuttle from 11F to 3R made for easy headland turns, and a skip function allowed the driver to shift two gears at a time, by simply tapping the toggle twice.

If all this seemed too complex (or expensive) you could still have a 9000 with a relatively simple 12-speed Syncro or 24-speed PowrSync, but neither had the Automatic Power Shift's sophistication. There was still a rubber track option as well, on the top three models, commanding a premium (in Britain) of around £30,000. A popular option in North America, but less so in Europe,

Below: John Deere followed Caterpillar with its own rubber track system. Caterpillar were not impressed and threatened that it would sue for breach of patent.

largely thanks to the fixed track center of 2.7 meters—with 900mm wide tracks (760mm was an option) this made the big Deere a little unwieldy for English country lanes. Having tracks of course, also meant that the big 9000 could not pivot steer.

There were five 9000s in all: 280hp 9120, 325hp 9220, 375hp 9320, 425hp 9420, and 450hp 9520. All were powered by a variation on John Deere's PowerTech six-cylinder diesel, the 9120 in 496ci (8.1 liter) guise, the others with the full-size 767ci (12.5 liter) version. All had substantially more power than in the 9010, thanks to electronic unit injectors, a higher compression ratio, new intake manifold and revised camshaft with higher lift. John Deere claimed lower emissions for the latest PowerTech as well. Electronics—where would the modern tractor be without them?

Right: A wheeled 9020, with a transmission so sophisticated that it could talk (politely) to the engine.

Below: The imposing 9520T—a far cry from the modest Model D, you have to wonder what John Deere the blacksmith would have made of this?

4010

SPECIFICATIONS

John Deere 4710 (2003)

Engine type Four-cylinder, water-cooled

Fuel type Diesel

Capacity 134ci (2.2 liters)

Rated speed 2,600rpm

TRANSMISSION

Transmission type PowrReverser

Speeds 12F/12R

Option eHydro/3 Range

DIMENSIONS

Factory weight 3,467lb

Wheelbase 71.5in

Hitch Category I

PERFORMANCE

Power (rated) 41hp

Power (at flywheel) 48hp

Turn radius 94.8in

Hydraulic capacity 15.9gpm

Above: Front loaders were a popular option on the 4000, and of course John Deere made sure to offer these itself—more profit for both factory and dealer.

Five years on from its original launch, John Deere's home grown compact tractor got its first big update as the 4010. Most of the fundamentals were unchanged, but buyers now had a bigger range to choose from. The line up comprised of nine tractors in all, stretching from 18hp to 48hp. Perhaps one of the biggest changes introduced to the upgraded range was that the 4000 now came in three chassis sizes to suit its power.

Smallest was the 18hp 4010, but the specification belied its size. Powered by a liquid-cooled diesel, it offered shift-on-the-go four-wheel-drive, a differential lock, and two independent PTOs, one was located in the middle, the other in the rear of the tractor. John Deere emphasized the ease of use of the hydrostatic transmission, which allowed changes of speed between forward and reverse, without clutching or shifting.

In this class of tractor, safety and ease of use are often the prime selling points. So these models included power assisted steering as well, plus an added technological bonus called Auto-Bleed—if the tractor ran out of fuel, its system didn't need to be bled before it could be restarted, as is otherwise the case with diesels. Just refill and go, as the adverts might well have said. It was no toy tractor though, coming with a Category I three-point hitch, 5.7gpm hydraulics, and the option of an iMatch quick-hitch.

The 4110 and 4115 offered much the same package, but with 20hp and 24hp power specifications respectively. These all had the small chassis, but next step up was the 4210 with mid-sized chassis, 28hp, and the option of two-

or four-wheel-drive. The same tractor with 32hp was a 4310, and the 4410 had 35hp and standard four-wheel-drive. Finally, with the large chassis, came the two-wheel-drive 4510 (39hp), two- or four-wheel-drive 4610 (44hp), and last, but by no means least, the range topping four-wheel-drive 4710 (48hp).

Like the 4010, Deere's compact flagship tractor had a relatively high-tech specification. With higher capacity hydraulics (15.9gpm) it could easily to cope with the Category I hitch and Quik Park loader.

One interesting option was the eMatch system. This brought several features, including Load Match, which provided automatic adjustment of the transmission to maintain power at the wheels. Speed Match would maintain a preset speed over rough ground, and Motion Match permitted adjustment of the rate at which the tractor slowed down— "fast" for quick shuttle cycles, "slow" for smoother stops. Finally Cruise Control would keep a preset speed, up hill and down.

That is a lot of technology, what would John Deere the blacksmith have said?

Top: The 4000 compact series was designed for grounds maintenance, rather than agricultural field work.

Left: Good visibility, thanks to a glassy "green house" cab, essential for work with a front loader.

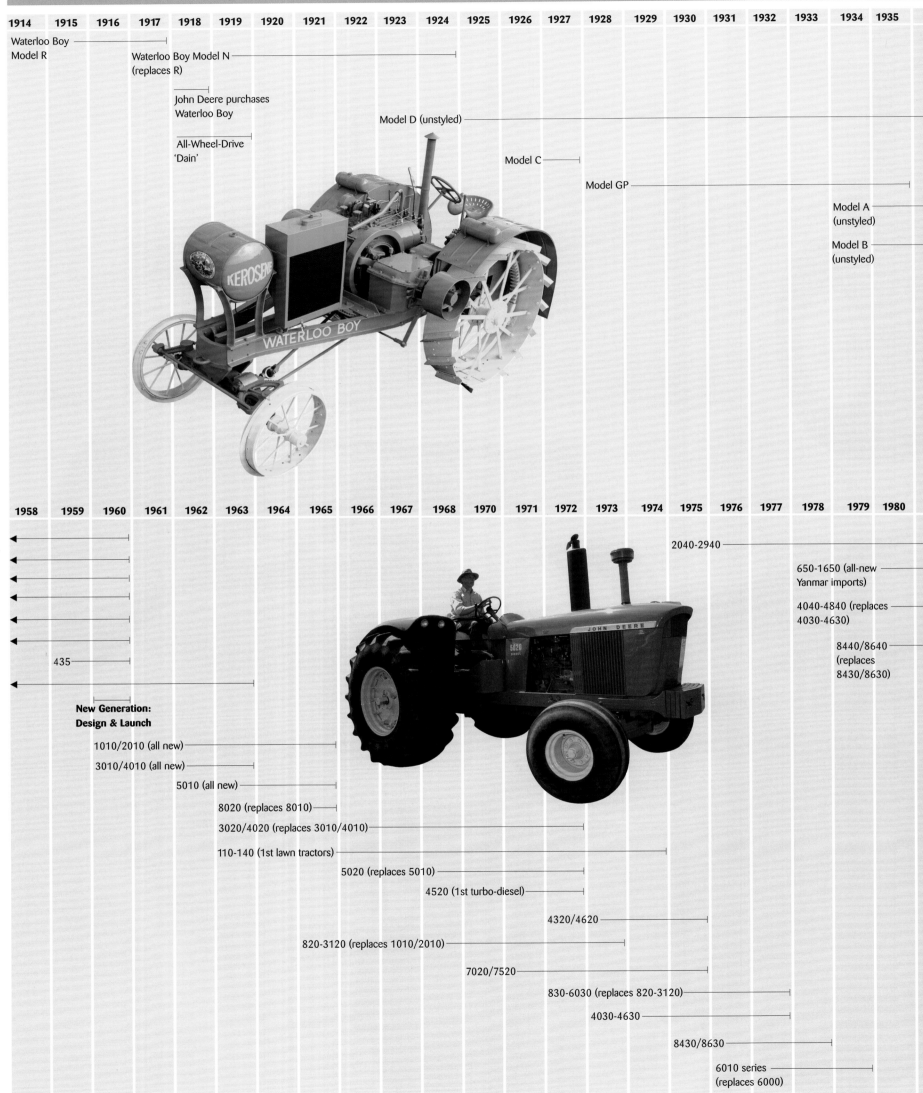

1914	1915	1916	1917	1918	1919	1920	1921	1922	1923	1924	1925	1926	1927	1928	1929	1930	1931	1932	1933	1934	1935

Waterloo Boy
Model R

Waterloo Boy Model N
(replaces R)

John Deere purchases
Waterloo Boy

All-Wheel-Drive
'Dain'

Model D (unstyled)

Model C

Model GP

Model A
(unstyled)

Model B
(unstyled)

1958	1959	1960	1961	1962	1963	1964	1965	1966	1967	1968	1970	1971	1972	1973	1974	1975	1976	1977	1978	1979	1980

2040-2940

650-1650 (all-new
Yanmar imports)

4040-4840 (replaces
4030-4630)

8440/8640
(replaces
8430/8630)

435

New Generation:
Design & Launch

1010/2010 (all new)

3010/4010 (all new)

5010 (all new)

8020 (replaces 8010)

3020/4020 (replaces 3010/4010)

110-140 (1st lawn tractors)

5020 (replaces 5010)

4520 (1st turbo-diesel)

4320/4620

820-3120 (replaces 1010/2010)

7020/7520

830-6030 (replaces 820-3120)

4030-4630

8430/8630

6010 series
(replaces 6000)

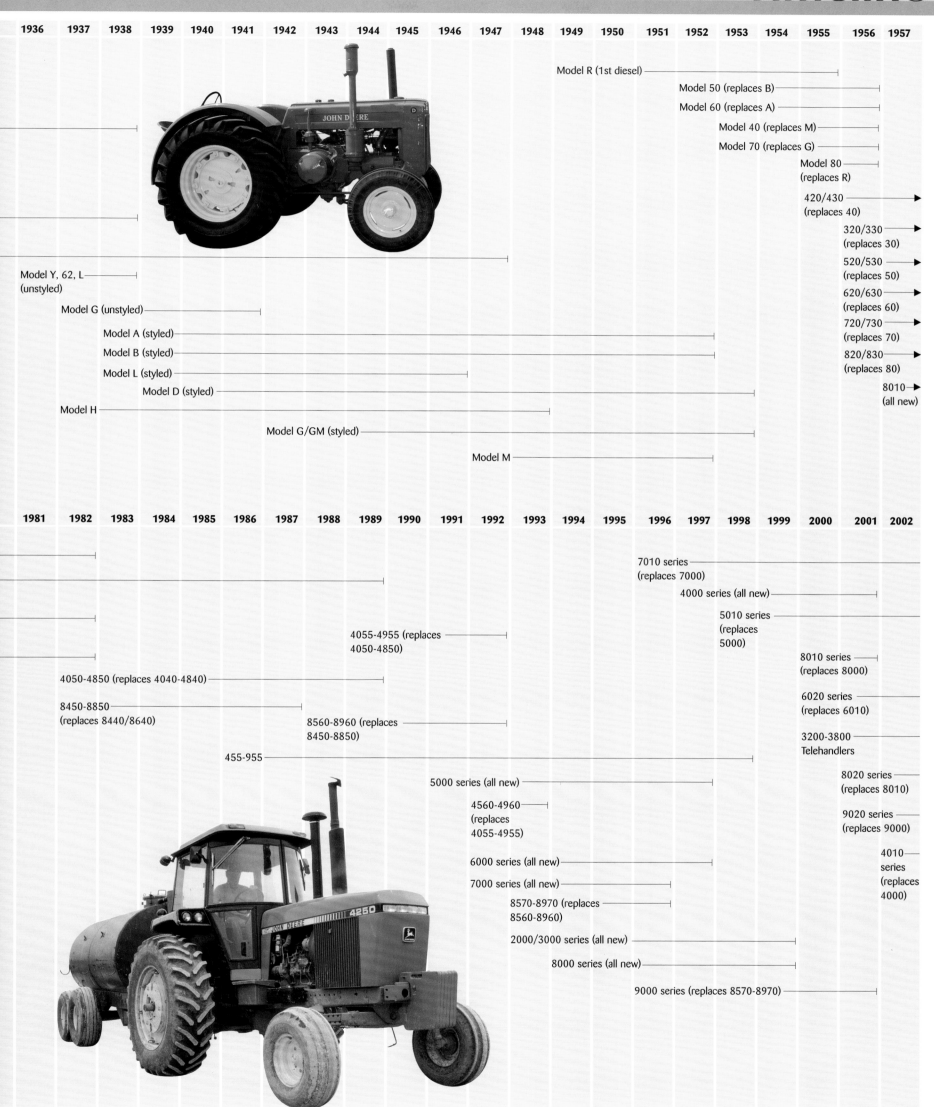

1936	1937	1938	1939	1940	1941	1942	1943	1944	1945	1946	1947	1948	1949	1950	1951	1952	1953	1954	1955	1956	1957

Model R (1st diesel)

Model 50 (replaces B)

Model 60 (replaces A)

Model 40 (replaces M)

Model 70 (replaces G)

Model 80 (replaces R)

420/430 (replaces 40)

320/330 (replaces 30)

520/530 (replaces 50)

620/630 (replaces 60)

720/730 (replaces 70)

820/830 (replaces 80)

8010 (all new)

Model Y, 62, L (unstyled)

Model G (unstyled)

Model A (styled)

Model B (styled)

Model L (styled)

Model D (styled)

Model H

Model G/GM (styled)

Model M

1981	1982	1983	1984	1985	1986	1987	1988	1989	1990	1991	1992	1993	1994	1995	1996	1997	1998	1999	2000	2001	2002

7010 series (replaces 7000)

4000 series (all new)

5010 series (replaces 5000)

8010 series (replaces 8000)

6020 series (replaces 6010)

3200-3800 Telehandlers

8020 series (replaces 8010)

9020 series (replaces 9000)

4010 series (replaces 4000)

4055-4955 (replaces 4050-4850)

4050-4850 (replaces 4040-4840)

8450-8850 (replaces 8440/8640)

8560-8960 (replaces 8450-8850)

455-955

5000 series (all new)

4560-4960 (replaces 4055-4955)

6000 series (all new)

7000 series (all new)

8570-8970 (replaces 8560-8960)

2000/3000 series (all new)

8000 series (all new)

9000 series (replaces 8570-8970)

Index

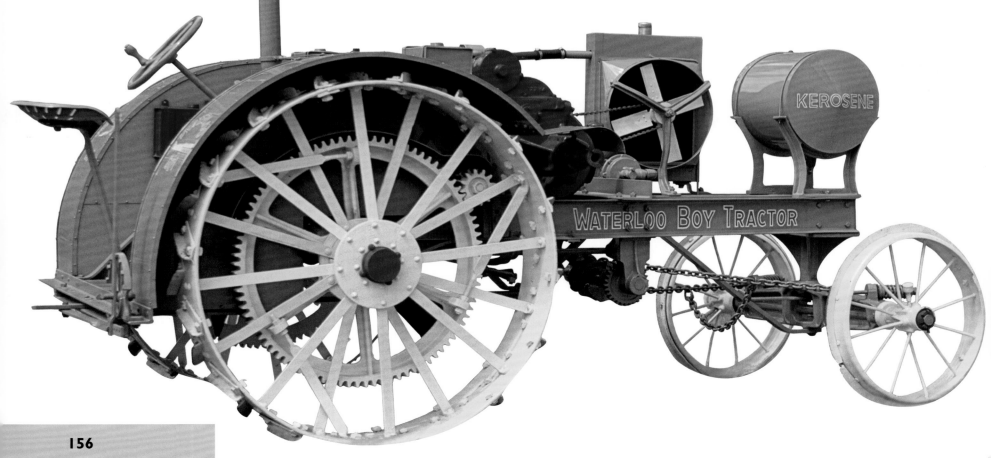

Credits

Picture Credits

All pictures are courtesy of © Deere & Company Archives, except for the following:

Garry Stuart ©
Pages: 5, 6-7, 17 (top), 22-23, 24-25, 28, 29 (top & bottom), 30, 31(top & bottom), 33 (bottom), 34-35, 36, 38, 41, 42-43, 46, 47, 48, 51 (top), 52, 55, 56 (top), 60-61, 64-65, 66, 67 (top & bottom), 68, 72, 74, 76, 78, 82-83, 84, 86, 90, 99 (top), 100, 102, 111 (top), 154 (bottom), 155 (top).

Andrew Morland ©
Pages: 40, 53 (top & bottom), 58, 62, 92, 94, 95 (bottom), 98 (bottom), 99 (bottom), 101 (top & bottom), 103, 106, 107 (top), 108, 109, 110, 112, 113 (bottom), 155 (bottom).

Randy Leffingwell ©
Pages: 19 (top & bottom), 70, 71 (top), 89 (top & bottom).

Peter Love ©
Pages: 14, 15 (top), 26, 27 (top), 55 (bottom), 59 (bottom), 80, 93 (bottom), 96.

Acknowledgements

This book was only made possible with the help of a great many people, so thanks go to the Deere & Company Archives (www.deere.com), who supplied many of the pictures used. A special vote of thanks must also go to Steve Mitchell at Pharo Communications Ltd. (www.pharoweb.co.uk), who helped to source and organize the images from the Deere & Company Archives. Also to photographers Andrew Morland, Garry Stuart, Randy Leffingwell, and Peter Love, who filled in the few gaps not covered by the John Deere archive. The team at MBI and Chrysalis Books, who took the book through some tight deadlines. And to my wife Anna, for her endless patience.

Note
Most of the specifications and figures in this book are taken from the tractor tests undertaken by the University of Nebraska, which began in 1920 and became a world authority for standardized tractor testing. Others come from John Deere, and some from *Profi* magazine. Inevitably, some discrepancies will arise between different sources.

Bibliography

Gay, Larry, *Farm Tractors 1975-1995*, ASAE, 1995
Gray, R.B., *The Agricultural Tractor 1855-1950*, ASAE, 1975
Larsen, Lester, *Farm Tractors 1950-1975*, ASAE, 1981
Macmillan, Don & Jones, Russell, *John Deere Tractors & Equipment* <u>Vol.1 1837-1959</u>, ASAE, 1996
Macmillan, Don, *The Field Guide to John Deere Tractors*, Japonica Press, 2002
Macmillan, Don & Harrington, Roy, *John Deere Tractors & Equipment* <u>Vol. 2 1960-1990</u>, ASAE, 1991
Morland, Andrew & Henshaw, Peter, *Modern Farm Tractors*, Motorbooks International, 1997
Peterson Jr., Chester & Beemer, Rod, *John Deere New Generation Tractors*, MBI, 1998
Profi International Magazine (various), Unique Magazines, part of the Mills Group Ltd.
Wendel, C.H., *Nebraska Tractor Tests since 1920*, Motorbooks International, 1993